PRACTICAL GUIDES

PHYSICAL

TEACHING WITHIN THE

NATIONAL CURRICULUM

PAULINE WETTON

Published by Scholastic Publications Ltd,
Villiers House, Clarendon Avenue,
Leamington Spa, Warwickshire, CV32 5PR

©1992 Scholastic Publications Ltd

Reprinted 1993

Written by Pauline Wetton
Edited by Juliet Gladston
Sub-edited by Jo Saxelby
Designed by Sue Limb
Illustrated by Rhian Nest James (Maggie Mundy)
Front cover designed by Lynne Joesbury
Front cover illustration by Jane Smith
Photographs by David Johnson (pages 5, 35, 67, 85 and 145), Sally and Richard Greenhill (Photographers Photolibrary) (page 11), Brian Godsby (page 55), A.L. Berry (Spectrum Colour Library) (page 81), Mike Turner (page 115), Keir Francis (page 135), M.J. Pooler (page 173), Maureen Firth (page 181), Bob Bray (page 199)

Every attempt has been made to trace and acknowledge the photographers whose pictures appear in this book. The publisher apologises for any omissions.

Designed using Aldus Pagemaker
Processed by Typesetters, Birmingham
Artwork by David Harban Design, Warwick
Printed in Great Britain by Ebenezer Baylis & Son, Worcester

The publishers wish to thank the Controller of Her Majesty's Stationery Office for permission to quote copyright material.

British Library Cataloguing in Publication Data
A catalogue record for this book is available from the British Library.

IBSN 0-590-53020-8

Contents

Introduction

Physical education in the National Curriculum

Although physical education is one of the last foundation subjects to be implemented as part of the National Curriculum, it is by no means the least important. In fact, it could be argued that it is one of the most essential parts since it is the only subject which is concerned exclusively with the 'physical' child. Consequently, and for the sake of their health, it is extremely important that all children are given a broad and balanced physical education curriculum. If teachers are able to do this, then many of the complaints suggesting that young people are physically inactive will be rejected.

The most important part of any physical education programme is that which gives children exercise. There are many reasons why exercise is important, three of which are given below.

• Exercise is essential for physical growth, development and the promotion of the healthy function of all the various body systems.

• Regular physical activity leads to greater mechanical strength in children's bones and muscles (Weltman *et al.*, 1986).

• Exercise improves the heart and cardiovascular system which in turn helps to improve stamina and functional capacity (Powell *et al.*, 1987 and Sports Council, 1988).

Unfortunately, recent studies have revealed the fact that most British children do not take up the opportunity for regular, vigorous exercise either in school or out of school hours and this probably contributes to their low levels of fitness (Sleap and Warburton, 1990 and Welsh Heart Programme Directorate, 1987). A report which suggests that children spend, on average, about three hours a day watching television seems to indicate that they think there are better things to do (BARB/AGB

5

Report, 1987). Priorities in programmes of study for physical education, therefore, need not only to help children exercise, but also to help them build up positive attitudes to exercise as well. Clearly, this will only be achieved if all teachers endeavour to make physical education lessons enjoyable and satisfying. In this way children will not only develop self-esteem, but may also adopt the exercise 'habit' which could stay with them for life.

The attainment target

The National Curriculum for physical education in the primary school is divided into two key stages. Broadly speaking, Key Stage 1 covers Years 1 and 2 in the infant school, while Key Stage 2 is concerned with children in Years 3, 4, 5 and 6 in the junior school. The principal requirement in the

statutory order, *Physical Education in the National Curriculum* (1992), is that there will be one attainment target which shall be: **'the sum total of all the end of key stage statements. In meeting the attainment target pupils should be able to demonstrate the knowledge, skills and understanding involved in [the six] areas of activity.'**
The end of key stage statements for Key Stage 1 state:
'Pupils should be able to:
(a) plan and perform safely a range of simple actions and linked movements in response to given tasks and stimuli.
(b) practise and improve their performance.
(c) describe what they and others are doing.
(d) recognise the effects of physical activities on their bodies.'
For Key Stage 2 there are six end of key stage statements:
'Pupils should be able to:
(a) plan, practise, improve and remember more complex sequences of movement.
(b) perform effectively in activities requiring quick decision making.
(c) respond safely, alone and with others, to challenging tasks, taking account of levels of skill and understanding.
(d) swim unaided at least 25 metres and demonstrate an understanding of water safety.
(e) evaluate how well they and others perform and behave against criteria suggested by the teacher, and suggest ways of improving performance.
(f) sustain energetic activity over appropriate periods of time in a range of physical activities and understand the effects of exercise on the body.'

Programmes of study

There are six areas of study in Key Stages 1 and 2: athletic activities, dance, games, gymnastic activities, outdoor and adventurous activities and swimming. In addition, *Physical Education in the National*

Curriculum (1992) lists the following requirements which should be applied to all key stages and be taught through all areas of activity. **'In physical education lessons pupils should be taught to:**
- **be physically active;**
- **demonstrate knowledge and understanding mainly through physical actions rather than verbal explanations;**
- **be aware at the same time of terminology relevant to activities undertaken; and**
- **engage in activities that involve the whole body, maintain flexibility and develop strength and endurance.**

In order to become independent learners pupils should be enabled to:
- **solve for themselves the problems that they will encounter in the course of their physical activities;**
- **evaluate initial attempts and decide how to modify subsequent attempts; and**
- **consolidate particular skills through practice and repetition.**

In order to develop positive attitudes pupils should be encouraged to:
- **observe the conventions of fair play, honest competition and good sporting behaviour;**
- **understand and cope with a variety of outcomes, including both success and failure;**
- **be aware of the effects and consequences of their actions on others and the environment; and**
- **appreciate the strengthsand be aware of the weaknesses of both themselves and others in relation to different activities.**

To ensure safe practice pupils should be taught to:
- **be concerned with their own and others' safety in all activities undertaken;**
- **understand th importance of warming up for, and recovery from, exercise, thus preventing injury;**
- **adopt good posture and the correct use of the body at all times;**
- **lift, carry and place equipment safely;**
- **observe the rules of good hygiene;**
- **understand the safety risks of wearing inappropriate clothing, footwear and jewellery; and**
- **respond readily to instructions and signals within established routines and follow relevant rules and codes.'**

It is quite clear that the statutory order will produce important implications for schools in general and teachers in particular.
- How will they work to meet the end of key stage statements?
- How can children with special needs be helped to meet these statements successfully?
- How will they teach two new areas of activity for Key Stage 1 children?
- How can all these areas be timetabled so that they fit in with the whole curriculum?
- What additional resources will be needed if the physical education curriculum is to be properly implemented?

End of key stage statements

The end of key stage statements have been worded so as to allow for 'a wide range of interpretation' (*PE for ages 5 to 16*, 1991). This implies that all schools will need to have a very clear idea of what they want their children to achieve in physical education. In a rather vague way, the statutory framework suggests that it is, 'sufficiently broad and flexible to allow schools discretion' (*PE for ages 5 to 16*, 1991). This would seem to mean that schools will need to look very carefully at the programmes of study, both to see what is expected and to ascertain the help they will require in order to achieve their goals for physical education. The non-statutory guidance (1992) which has been produced by the National Curriculum Council should become a helpful resource for teachers in meeting the the requirements of the stututory order for physical education. The guidance covers four areas which teachers will need to consider very carefully: planning and implementation; progression; assessment and special educational needs. The guidance therefore gives detailed information about an important responsibility which both schools and teachers will have to build into their planning, that being the consideration of those children with special needs: 'The text of the end of key stage statements, programmes of study and examples is written and designed to make the physical education curriculum accessible to as many pupils as possible with little or no interpretation or modification for pupils with Special Educational Needs.'

Children with special needs

For the first time in the history of physical education, a national curriculum now provides a legal framework in which all children, regardless of any impairment, will have an entitlement to a broad and balanced physical education programme, within mainstream education, which is relevant to their needs. As a result, all schools will have to consider writing a special educational needs policy for physical education so that it can be included in their whole school planning for these children.

A useful way to start such planning would be to read the document, *Physical Education for ages 5 to 16,* DES (1991, HMSO). In the light of this, schools ought to review their intended physical education programme and identify those children who would be considered to have special needs. It is important, when considering such children, to become knowledgeable about their impairments, to concentrate on their abilities, to have a positive attitude

about providing a challenging programme for them and, above all, to consider how tasks, equipment, playing areas and access can be modified so that they can have a meaningful experience. In order to help them to do this, schools should seek out advice and help from those who can give them support, especially ancillary staff, parents and outside agencies such as leisure services, Sports Development Officers, the British Sports Association for the Disabled (see Resources section, page 207), the governing bodies for the various sports or the local education authority's special needs adviser.

In all the planning, the most important point to remember is that disabled children must be given the opportunity, wherever possible, to be active alongside their able-bodied colleagues.

Two new areas of activity for Key Stage 1

Another 'first' which schools and teachers will have to accomodate in their programmes for Key Stage 1 is in providing for athletic activities and for outdoor and adventurous activities. There are many implications involved in planning for both of these new ventures and these will be discussed later in the book (see Chapters 3 and 5). However, it may be worth pointing out that athletics, for example, may be subsumed into a games programme, or alternatively, may form a discrete unit by itself, to be enjoyed in the summer months.

Timetabling

With all the pressures which implementing the 'new' curriculum for physical education will bring, one of the most obvious for schools could be in the area of timetabling. As there are now six discrete areas of study to manage, schools will need a clear policy on when these activities can take place. The proposals from the Physical Education Working Group were quite specific when

they recommended that children in Key Stages 1 and 2 should experience gymnastic activities, games and dance in each week throughout the school year (see 8.33 PE for ages 5 to 16, 1991). It was also pointed out, again by the Working Group, that evidence had shown that children benefit from short daily lessons. So how will this affect planning?

One solution might be to consider offering specific blocks of time in designated terms so that the requirements of the statutory orders for, say, swimming and outdoor and adventurous activities could be met, but the problem of timetabling will not easily be overcome.

Resources

Hand in hand with the difficulties of timetabling activities for PE goes the question of resources. While it is illuminating to hear both HMI and other sources claiming that, 'given imaginative use of accomodation a high percentage of schools have the physical resources to make the recommendations in the statutory orders work' (PE for ages 5 to 16, 1991) many primary schools will still face the perpetual difficulty of having only one big space indoors which is suitable for PE and which is in regular competition with either television programmes, singing practices, school lunches or a combination of all three! So, unless school halls are restored to their original purposes, it is quite clear that it will often not be possible to timetable the number of activities listed in the proposals or use the hall exclusively for implementing them. Therefore, the playground too will have to be used especially for games.

Equipment resourcing is also essential. Obviously, careful stock taking for PE will be of paramount importance when spending money – to ensure that all the essential apparatus is available for both disabled and able-bodied children, and any necessary trips to swimming pools and activity centres covered.

Programme planning and assessment

Much of the responsibility for what has been discussed so far would appear to rest with those who implement school policy. However, individual teachers will also be faced with difficult decisions as they seek to prioritise their programmes. They will have to think carefully about planning the content of this extended and progressive curriculum and to offer differentiated tasks to satisfy the learning and exercise needs of a wide range of physical abilities which each class will present. Then there is the question of assessment which will be the responsibility of each class teacher. However, assessment in PE should not become an unduly onerous task. 'End of key stage statements provide the framework for making assessments, planning the next stage of learning and reporting to parents. They will also help to inform teachers in the same or other schools about a pupil's attainment' (*Non-statutory Guidance,* 1992). Section F in the non-statutory guidance gives teachers some very useful information on the criteria to use in assessing a pupil's performance, on methods of collecting evidence pf a pupil's attainment and on recording procedures.

The book

This book is intended to provide a suggested syllabus for physical education in the National Curriculum for primary children in Key Stage 1 and Key Stage 2 and relates closely to the requirements of the curriculum. The quotes that are given in bold throughout the book are all taken from the DES document, *Physical Education in the National Curriculum* (1992, HMSO).

Chapters 1 to 5 form a comprehensive and complete scheme of work for five of the six areas of study for children in Key Stage 1, while Chapters 6 to 10 form a similar scheme for Key Stage 2. The chapters have been arranged in this order to provide easy access for class teachers of each phase, but they can be looked at as a whole, since together, they form a complete and progressive scheme running across the primary age range from Reception to Year 6.

Chapter 11 (Swimming) however, provides a complete scheme of work across the whole age range. This is in accordance with the National Curriculum which states that children may be taught to swim in either Key Stage 1 or Key Stage 2 or across both phases.

Finally, Chapter 12 looks at the cross-curricular issues which have been identified as whole school concerns in the National Curriculum documentation.

Where it is appropriate, evaluation sheets are provided at the end of the chapters. These sheets can be photocopied and used either as an ongoing record of achievement for each child or to form the basis of an evaluation tool for each school's discussion about assessment procedures.

You will find full bibliographic references, information about other relevant publications and useful addresses in the Resources section at the end of the book (pages 207 and 208).

Key Stage 1

Chapter 1
Gymnastic activities

'Gymnastic activities focus on the body. They are concerned with acquiring control, co-ordination and versatility in the use of the body, and responding to challenges. They are based on natural actions such as leaping, balancing, inverting, rolling and swinging. At the primary stage a variety of each is experienced, explored, practiced, refined, adapted and consolidated. Some named gymnastic skills will be developed in this context. Pupils improve their performance and are able to apply their skilfulness in new contexts. They learn to work on the floor and on apparatus and to compose sequences of movement which show appropriate dynamic qualities, fluency and control' (*National Curriculum Physical Education Working Group Interim Report,* 1991).

This chapter is intended to be used as a programme of study for gymnastic activities in Key Stage 1. It is based around working through a number of movement themes which will incorporate **'the basic actions of travelling, turning, rolling, jumping, balancing, swinging, climbing and taking weight on hands both on the floor and using apparatus'** (Programme of Study), in other words, the physical skills which pupils in Key Stage 1 are required to experience in this area of the National Curriculum.

Six themes: travelling; body shape; jumping and landing; weight bearing leading to balance; rolling and sliding; and working with partners, have been selected to provide the sound foundation both for gymnastic performance and the acquisition of the required skills stated above. These themes are presented in a particular order to ensure the continuity and progression which is essential in delivering the National Curriculum. However, the material has not been classified into the defined age groups since both children's growth and changes in physical ability are at their greatest during Key Stages 1 and 2.

When working on a particular movement theme you should make sure you include:
• working at different levels;
• variation in the speed of movement;
• movement in different directions;
• movement quality.

A gymnastic theme may take a few weeks or a few months to complete, depending on its content, the ability of the children and the time spent on gymnastics each week.

Safety in gymnastics

It is vital that you have access to the official document, *Safe Practice in Physical Education* (1990), produced by the British Association of Advisers and Lecturers in Physical Education. This document is used as an important reference on the rare occasions when charges of negligence are brought against teachers and therefore it is important to read this publication before creating any new policies for physical education in your school.

The document stresses:
• the need to make sure that all staff are qualified and trained to teach safely;
• the need to check equipment regularly;
• the need to ensure that children have the necessary strength and skills to undertake tasks;
• the need to make sure that children are suitably dressed, wearing clothes that do not restrict movement, but are not too loose, that they are not wearing jewellery and have long hair tied back;
• the need to ensure that children either wear suitable, purpose-designed gym shoes or have bare feet – trainers with hard plastic soles should not be worn;

• that children should never be allowed to play chasing games where they use gymnastic equipment as obstacles.

Structuring lessons

Gymnastic lessons should be divided into four parts: warm-up, floorwork, apparatus work and cool-down. Every session should begin by getting the children to warm-up. Essentially, this should consist of a slow build-up to energetic easy movements in an effort to increase the heart rate, the rate of breathing and to stretch the muscles to increase flexibility. Before, during and after the warm-up section of a session, take the opportunity to reinforce the children's understanding of the meaning of being 'hot' and 'cold' in relation to the temperature of their bodies. This can be developed throughout the whole of Key Stage 1 and in doing so, will automatically fulfil the requirement of the attainment target which states that **'pupils should be able to recognise the effects of physical activity on their bodies'** (End of Key Stage 1 Statement).

Even though the following six themes each have a suggested warm-up you can choose from them the warm-up which you consider to be most appropriate for your class. If one warm-up becomes a favourite, use it as often as you like! Each warm-up listed in the text will ensure the necessary 'tuning up' of the body for all the themes.

After the warm-up the children can move on to floorwork. This should consist of a series of tasks completed without apparatus where the children learn skills and create movement patterns in response to ideas within the theme. The children can then work with apparatus. In the early sessions, the children should work with intermediary apparatus, such as mats, benches and hoops in order to develop their floorwork patterns. However, as their skills increase they can move on to incorporating suitable large apparatus, such as boxes and wall bars, which will allow them to develop their floorwork patterns on the apparatus. Try to ensure that the children put out the apparatus themselves. Show all the class how to carry and manoeuvre each piece of apparatus. Show them where and how to grip each piece of apparatus, how to lift it and which way to face as they carry it. Follow these demonstrations by telling the children how to place the apparatus safely on the ground. This will involve co-operation between the children as they ensure that apparatus is grounded simultaneously, gently and with control. It will take them a considerable time, but this is time really well spent. You can note which children listen to instructions and perhaps, more ominously, those who do not! Leadership and co-operative skills frequently become obvious when children are involved in moving apparatus.

It is highly likely that in the first large apparatus lesson the children might only have a few minutes on the apparatus and then have to put it all away again. If this is so, praise and encourage them while reminding them that they will be getting these pieces out and putting them away every week. Also let them know that they will be working with the same group. Doing and saying all this, not only gives the children advance knowledge of the structure of the lesson, but also provides an essential framework which younger children need. Eventually, the children will be able to work on other apparatus and perhaps choose which apparatus they would like to work on for themselves.

As the theme develops, the children should be presented with 'movement tasks' which give them the opportunity to work at their own level of ability and which give them the chance to choose movements which are within their own capabilities. Most importantly, each group of children should be allowed to work on the apparatus before being given a task. This will enable them to become familiar with the texture, width, length and height of the apparatus. Once this preliminary work has been done, the children can be presented with some specific tasks.

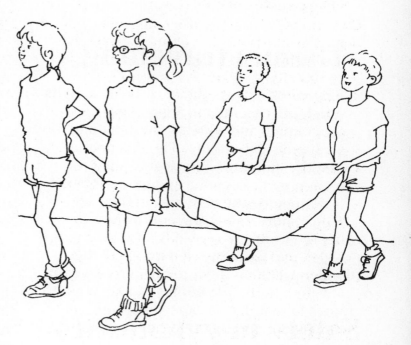

Finally, end the session with a period of cool-down. This is an important activity, calming the children down, allowing a gradual cooling of the muscles, the slow contraction of the blood vessels and the return of the body to its normal functioning. Suggestions are provided for cool-down activities on page 32 that are suitable for all six themes.

The amount of time spent on each part in the lesson will, of course, be discretionary, but a useful guideline for a 30 minute lesson would be:
• five minutes of warm-up;
• ten minutes of floorwork;
• ten minutes of apparatus work;
• five minutes cool-down.

As a particular theme develops and the children have explored, practised and refined their movement patterns, then more time should be spent on the

apparatus. The lesson would probably then be structured:
- five minutes of warm-up;
- twenty minutes of apparatus work;
- five minutes of cool-down.

Theme: travelling

'Travelling' covers the most basic actions which are essential to a gymnastic programme and which form the foundation of all physical activity. There is no doubt that the immature physical form of the reception class child can be developed by experiencing the activities in this section. 'The children's natural enthusiasm for being physically active' (*PE for ages 5 to 16*, 1991), can be harnessed into activities which will help them to begin to develop strength in their lower limbs and begin to be able to judge the speed of their movement and that of other people.

Warm-up

Explain to the children at the outset of the activities the importance of warming-up their bodies, so that they can begin to understand that this part of the lesson is intended to 'prepare the body for exercise and prevent injury (*PE for ages 5 to 16*, 1991). The children can then carry out the following warm-up exercises.
- Ask the children to walk on their toes, stretch their arms high in the air and then curl up and walk. Repeat this exercise about five times.
- Tell the children to lift one knee high and then lift the other knee high. They can then do this to the accompaniment of 'Knees up Mother Brown', working through the song twice for about 30 seconds.
- Ask the children to kneel down and then stretch up high. They should do this about five times.
- Tell the children to put their hands and feet on the floor. They should each lift one hand high, then put it down again and lift the other hand high. Ask them to lift one leg high, put it down again and then lift the

other leg high. Let them do this five times.
- Ask the children to lie on their backs and stretch, and then lie on their fronts and stretch. They should repeat this five times.
- Ask the children to kneel down, lie down and then stand up. They can repeat this five times.

Floorwork

When the children are warmed-up, suggest various exercises that they can perform which will help them to become familiar with the notion of travelling. Ask them to explore:
- various methods of travelling on foot, for example walking, jogging, running, jumping, hopping and skipping;
- various modes of travelling, for example taking long steps or short steps, walking on tiptoe, heels and the sides of the feet;
- different speeds of travelling, for example slow, slower, fast, faster;
- various directions of travel, for example forwards, backwards or sideways;
- various levels of movement, for example near to the ground, medium height, high and away from the ground.

Even at this early stage in the natural development of children it will be possible to begin to help them to 'move from: dependence to independence in learning, from performing given tasks to being able to structure their own (*PE for ages 5 to 16*, 1991). Stimulate the children's own input by asking the following questions:
- Can you make a movement pattern which has walking, jumping and hopping in it?
- Can you repeat the pattern three times?
- Are you going quickly sometimes and slowly sometimes?
- Have you changed direction and have you thought about the level at which you are working?

Observe the children's creations and help individuals to improve their movement pattern. Select children who have made a simple but effective pattern and ask them to perform it for the rest of the class. In this way other children can be helped to understand how to fit their movements together. Also encourage the children to evaluate the quality of their peers' patterns. Again, even at this early stage, children can 'use given criteria to judge others' performance' (*PE for ages 5 to 16*, 1991) and can begin to develop observational skills enabling them to reach the attainment target which states that **'pupils should be able to: describe what they and others are doing...'** (End of Key Stage 1 Statement).

A good demonstration by a child is one of the most useful visual aids to teaching. Demonstrations not only help the children to develop their evaluation skills, but also can be used to reinforce good practice, to clarify or demonstrate a teaching point, to set a problem-solving situation, to widen movement vocabulary or to show children that there are many different ways of solving the original task. Care should be taken, however, at this stage, to concentrate on one teaching point at a time and to put the children into action immediately after the demonstration in order to ensure that good practice ensues. There can be no doubt that good standards are usually achieved in gymnastics if children are **'given opportunities to practice, adapt, and improve their control of individual actions'** (Programme of Study). Guidance and friendly encouragement should accompany this practice.

Once all the children can happily perform their movement patterns on the floor, it will be possible to introduce some apparatus. Hoops and mats are valuable intermediary pieces of equipment which focus the children's attention on a specific area, but do not challenge their physical competence beyond their capabilities.

Intermediary apparatus

Arrange the children into groups and show them how to lay out the hoops and mats.

It is very important for children, even at this, the earliest stage, to **'be taught to carry and position simple apparatus using the correct lifting technique'** (Programme

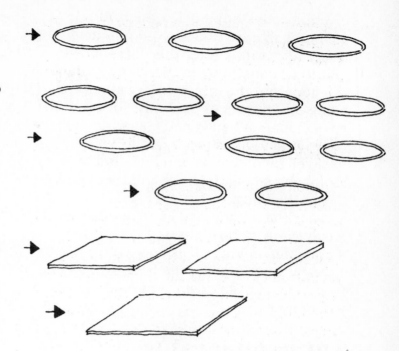

of Study). In fact this is an ideal time to instigate what should be a recognised procedure in all gymnastic lessons throughout their school lives. It must be remembered too that lifting, carrying and manoeuvring large pieces of equipment and furniture are important life skills which children should acquire at the earliest opportunity.

When the apparatus is in place (see above), ask the children to repeat the movement tasks which you introduced during the floorwork part of the session, for example ask them to practise walking in and out of the hoops or across the mats forwards/backwards/sideways or jumping in and out of the hoops or over the mats forwards/backwards/sideways.

Guide and help the children until they respond confidently, and then ask them to plan a movement pattern over, across and round the apparatus. You can stimulate their creativity by making a few constructive suggestions, for example, they might like to have a jumping pattern or a hopping pattern, or they might like to have a mixture of walking and jumping, or hopping and walking – they can choose.

The next stage in the development of the theme will be to introduce the children to other ways of travelling on foot, for

example sidestepping, leaping and galloping, before they move on to using the larger apparatus. After this, introduce the children to methods of travelling around the floor and the intermediary apparatus using other parts of the body, for example:
• travelling on hands and feet with feet together and apart;
• travelling on hands and feet, first with stomachs facing the floor and then backs facing the floor;
• travelling on one hand and one foot;
• travelling on bottoms and feet;
• crawling on lower legs and hands;
• pushing and pulling the body while lying face down, backs down, and on each side of the body.

Large apparatus

Having worked on intermediary apparatus, the children will be ready to move on to using larger apparatus. If there are enough benches and planks, it would be helpful for the children to go through the previous activities at a low height before being challenged with the plethora and variety of apparatus often arranged for them. The bench or plank is appropriate because it challenges the children to reduce the area in which they work. Initially, it does limit their range of movements, but at the same time it gives them the opportunity to try out possible activities which are appropriate to the equipment and about which they feel confident.

Choose apparatus which will allow the children to function within the theme. Select benches, planks, table tops – any piece which will give them an opportunity to practise the movement patterns which have already been refined on the floor (see the suggested apparatus layout below).

Movement tasks

Once the children have been given time to familiarise themselves with the apparatus, present them with the following specific tasks.
• 'Explore your apparatus: travel over it, under it, around it.'
• 'Move about your apparatus on your hands and feet.'
• 'Travel around and between your apparatus on your feet.'
• 'Travel on your apparatus on a different part of your body.'
• 'How many different parts of your body can you travel on?'
• 'Choose the travelling movements you like best and make a movement pattern over, along and around your apparatus. Can you vary the speed at which you travel? Are you making the best possible movements? Can you stretch more? Can you repeat your pattern? Where are you going to start? How are you going to finish?'

Talk to individual children about how they might improve their movement

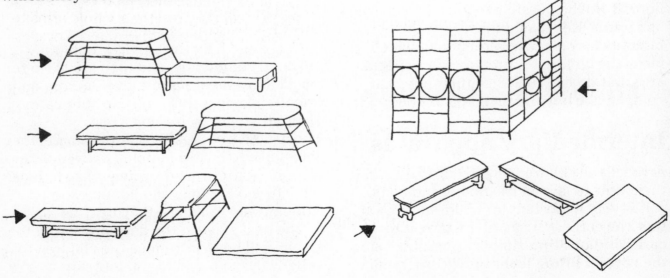

patterns to make the sequence of movements flow smoothly from one to the next. The children should be encouraged to practise their movement patterns until they are of good quality, demonstrating that their patterns have a good start, a good finish, a variety of movements and a variation of speeds. They should also be able to ensure that the shape of their body is always clear. For example, if the child has chosen a stretched shape as part of her movement pattern then her spine, arms, fingers, legs, feet and toes should be totally extended. Similarly, if a child has chosen a curled shape then his body should be totally 'tucked': head, spine, limbs and parts of limbs should be bent, flexed and folded in to the body.

The children should be encouraged to refine their movement patterns so that they can repeat them and, eventually, they should be ready to perform them to the rest of the class. After a performance, all the children who are spectators should participate in an evaluation process.

To encourage children to become confident in commenting on a performance, ask them questions which encourage them to communicate. The following are suggested starting points:
• Did you like the start of the performance/pattern? Can you tell me why? Was it the position of Sam's body which you liked?
• Which movements did you think had the clearest shape?
• Did you see any quick movements? Which were they?
• Can you suggest how the movement pattern could be improved?

Theme: body shape

It is important that children develop an awareness of the simple movements that can change their body shape. Stretching, curling and twisting, for example, form the basis of all human movement. In addition, by working through stretching, curling and twisting the children will improve and develop body flexibility which will allow

them a greater range of actions, and in turn will enable them to perform more complex actions. The PE Working Group stated clearly that, 'For every pupil the activity should involve the whole body and encourage the maintenance of flexibility and the development of strength' (*PE for ages 5 to 16*, 1991). These simple movements can be practised using different bases and while travelling over different surfaces. From their earliest gymnastic experiences children 'need to be made aware of the importance of good posture and the correct use of the body when performing apparently simple actions such as walking, sitting, pulling, pushing or lifting' (*PE for ages 5 to 16*, 1991). If children have been working intelligently on the activities associated with the theme of travelling then they will have begun to feel the muscle tension which is necessary to hold a good posture. As the movements increase in difficulty, they will need to become more aware of the muscle tension and control that such movements demand.

Warm-up

• Ask the children to alternate between jogging and walking as they travel about the room.
• Tell them to each make small circles in the air using both their index fingers and then to circle their wrists.
• Tell the children to each point and stretch both their feet and draw a circle on the floor and use their elbows to draw a circle. Can they use their whole arms to make large circles? They should circle forwards and backwards, using both their right and left arms.
• Ask the children to circle their shoulders forwards and backwards. Can they circle their pelvises?
• Ask the children to use their whole bodies to make the largest circle possible and then use their noses to make small circles.
• Ask the children to run around the room making small circles and then large clockwise and anticlockwise circles.

Floorwork

Once the children have worked through the warm-up exercises they can be introduced to the skills of stretching, curling and twisting which will help them when working on the movement tasks.

Stretching

• Ask the children first to each stretch their right arm high, then their left arm high and finally both arms high together. Tell them to stretch their fingers too.
• Ask the children to make long stretched shapes. Tell them to reach as high as possible with their arms and fingers.
• Can they make wide shapes? They should stretch their arms and legs as wide as possible.
• Ask the children to lie down on the floor and stretch their bodies, making long shapes and then wide shapes.
• Ask them to walk in their spaces on tiptoe, stretching their legs, bodies, arms and fingers to make long shapes.
• Tell the children to make wide shapes and try to walk around the room keeping those shapes.
• Ask them to sit down and stretch their arms and legs making star shapes.
• Ask the children to stretch their fingers wide and make spikey shapes.
• Tell them to lie on first their left and then their right sides and then on their backs and the front of their bodies and explore stretched shapes. They should lift one arm first, then one leg, then both their arms and legs off the floor together.

Curling

• Ask the children to stand on both feet and curl up, tucking in their arms and heads.
• Ask them to lie on the floor and curl up on their left sides, their right sides and then on their backs.
• Ask them to kneel on the lower part of their legs and curl up into ball shapes. Can they move around the space on their feet in

a curled shape, first walking, then jumping, using both feet?
• Ask the children to curl up on the floor on their left side and wrap their arms around their legs and hold them tightly. Tell them to rock on their back, on their right side and then from side to side.

Twisting

• Ask the children to stand on both feet and twist at the waist turning to the right and then to the left as far as possible without moving their feet.
• Ask them to kneel down on the lower part of their legs and twist to the right and then to the left.
• Ask them to face the floor and distribute their body weight evenly on both their hands and feet. Tell them to take one hand off the floor and thread it under the other arm, taking the twist as far as possible.

Combined movements

• Ask the children each to collect a hoop and place it on the floor in a space. They should then practise jogging round the room in the spaces around the hoops and when you call out 'curled shape', 'wide shape' or 'tall shape', they must make the relevant body shape inside the nearest hoop.
• Explain to the children that they must jog about the room and when you call, 'hedgehogs' they must continue to move about the room on their feet, but in a curled shape. When you call, 'lamposts' they must stretch as high as possible and move about the area on tiptoe. An additional fun element can be included if you call, 'dead ants'. On this command, the children should lie down on the floor on their backs with their arms and legs in the air.
• Ask the children to face the floor and curl up with their body weight on their hands and feet. Keeping some weight on their feet, they should try to walk their hands across the floor as far as possible, stretching out like a caterpillar. When they have made a

fully stretched shape, they should keep their hands still and walk their feet across the floor.

Once the children have had experience of moving in these different ways you can ask them to plan movement patterns of their own, based on the shape work. Stimulate the planning exercise by suggesting an outline, for example, 'We have practised making three shapes with our bodies while we have been taking our weight on different body parts. Now, I would like you to plan a movement pattern using curled small shapes, stretched long shapes, and wide star shapes.

You might like to think about starting off by making one of these shapes and then move into another shape. You might like to hold your shape, frozen like a statue, or you might like to move around the area keeping to a particular shape. You choose what you do, and I will come and help you.'

Intermediary apparatus

Mats

Mats are essential in gymnastics since they provide the gymnast with a soft, resilient surface to land on and also they allow the gymnast to practise a greater range of movements. Younger children may not have had an opportunity to work on a mat before, so the simple tasks which follow will help them to become familiar with the properties of this important piece of equipment. Children will, for instance, become aware of the mat's length and width, but more importantly its function as a supportive, resilient and soft base.
• Ask the children to walk across the mat using a stretched tall shape and then a curled small shape.
• Ask them to move across the mat on the lower part of their legs in a curled shape.
• Ask the children to each stand on one foot on the mat and make a stretched shape with their arms and legs.
• Ask them to each kneel on one knee and make a stretched shape with their other leg

and both arms.
• Ask them to curl into a ball shape on one side of their bodies and roll across the mats in a stretched shape, keeping their arms and legs off the mat.
• Ask the children to curl up on the mats and suddenly make a stretched shape and curl up suddenly and so on.

Benches

Benches are important and versatile pieces of equipment which often present children with their first real gymnastic challenge. It may be, for example, that it is the first time in gymnastics that they have been required to work at height on a restricted surface area. Their ability to control and to co-ordinate their movements on a reduced base will come as a real challenge to many of them.
• Ask the children to move along the bench on their feet in a curled shape, a tall shape and then a wide shape. Can they turn round and round, keeping the shape, and move along the bench?
• Ask them to move along the bench with long stretched strides.
• Ask the children to make their own shape and then move along the bench keeping their chosen shape.
• Ask them to practise a bunny jump over the bench. To do this, the child should stand at one side of the bench and place her hands in a gripping position with one hand on either side of the bench. To initiate the jump, all her body weight should be put on to her hands and her arms should be kept together as the hips are lifted to move the tucked legs over the bench.
• Ask the children to lie on the bench on the front of their bodies and practise pulling themselves along the bench in a stretched, long shape.
• Ask the children to choose their own body shapes and pull themselves along the bench in those shapes.
• Encourage the children to try making all the body shapes they can think of including irregular and twisted shapes and move across the apparatus in those shapes.

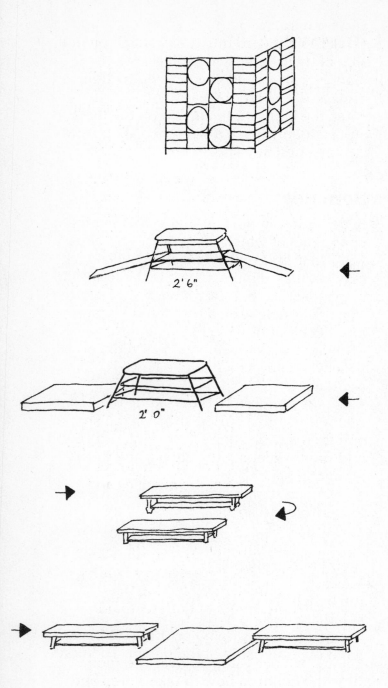

positioning their largest apparatus, until you tell them to collect, carry and position their mats. Check that there is enough space around the apparatus for safe approaches and landings and that there are no 'resident obstacles' such as pianos or bookcases which could be hazardous. (An apparatus layout is suggested opposite.)

Movement tasks

Choose one task for the children to work on in each lesson. The following list provides some movement task suggestions which the children should try out on all the pieces of apparatus.

• 'Explore your apparatus. Practise whatever you choose to do very carefully.'
• 'Travel across your apparatus and at some point show me two long or two stretched shapes on your apparatus.'
• 'See if you can stay in a curled shape as you move across your apparatus.'
• 'Make as many wide shapes as you can while you are on your apparatus.'
• 'Find out how many times you can make a wide shape with your legs.'
• 'Can you experiment and make a twisted shape or an irregular shape while you are on your apparatus?'
• 'Choose the movements and the shapes which you like best and link them together to make a pattern. Make your shapes clear so that I can see which one you are doing.'

Theme: jumping and landing

Jumping is probably the activity which physically competent children enjoy the most. Unfortunately, not all children are competent in this skill when they start school and so this theme should not be introduced until all the children have had some experience in a large activity area both on the floor and on apparatus. Landing the body weight from a height is quite a difficult function to which children should be introduced gradually.

Large apparatus

In the initial stages children should set out the apparatus cautiously and slowly. Each group of children should get out their apparatus in turn – a useful management strategy is to put out the largest pieces of equipment first, starting with the climbing frame, then the stacking tables, the benches and, finally, the mats. The children should stay with their own group in their designated working area after carrying and

Warm-up

• Ask the children to stretch high and tall, stretch out wide and then curl up small. The children should practise each shape and then alternate: tall, small, tall, wide and so on.

• Ask the children to walk about the room, making each shape in turn. Can they make these shapes when lying on the floor? They should change from tall and stretched, to wide and stretched, to curled up small. They can try these shapes facing the floor and then facing the ceiling.

• Ask the children to jump with both feet together on the spot. They can then jump around the room using both feet.
• Ask them to jump around the room on both feet in a small shape and then in a wide shape.

Floorwork

• Talk with the children about how their bodies bend and why we need to be able to bend. They will enjoy flexing and extending all the joints of their bodies and should practise identifying the proper names for each joint.
• Take the children on a 'body tour'. Tell them to bend at the waist and then bend each joint until they reach a crouched position. They should then sit down and bend the joints of their fingers, wrists and elbows. They should circle their wrists and shoulder joints, stretch their toes wide and then curl them up, stretch their feet and then bend each foot up and circle their ankle joints. Finally, explain about the composition of the spine and how the head is articulated. Encourage the children to feel the bones of their spines at the back of their necks and then ask them to feel the strong muscles which attach their heads to their spines. (If they turn their heads gently from side to side and then lift and lower their chins they will feel the muscles and their movements more clearly.)
• Tell the children to jump by gently bending their ankles and knees before taking off and springing into the air. They should catch their body weight by landing on their toes, quickly transferring the weight on to the whole of both feet and bending at their hips, knees and ankles.
• Ask the children to pretend to be a bouncing ball and jump all over the room.
• Show the children how to take a step and jump into the air and land safely. Let them practise it.
• Ask the children to run and jump into the air. Let them practise landing on one foot, closely followed by the other. You must continually emphasise the bending, sinking action which is necessary for safe landings. To practise a good take-off and a safe landing, arrange the children into pairs. One child in the pair should kneel and crouch as low as possible while his partner jumps over him.
• The children should now attempt to push-off from the floor where they are standing

so that they can jump high enough to stretch their arms, legs and feet in the air before landing safely.

Intermediary apparatus

Hoops

Ask the children to place a hoop in a space and then suggest the following movement tasks.
• Jump around the outside of the hoop on both feet.
• Hop around the outside of the hoop, first on one foot and then on the other.
• Use both feet to jump into the hoop and to jump out of the hoop. Can they do this while moving forwards and then backwards?
• Leap into the hoop from one foot, landing on the other foot and then leap out of the hoop.
• Run towards the hoop and step on to one foot and jump over the hoop landing on both feet.

Benches

When using benches to practise jumping and landing encourage the children to be cautious until they are fully aware of the height and width of the bench. Once they are familiar with these you can proceed with the following movement tasks.
• Ask the children to walk along the bench and step off carefully.
• Ask the children to walk along the bench and try to stretch in the air as they walk off, before landing.
• Ask the children to run along the bench and jump off the end.
   At this point, you should alert the children to the need to control their running speed before taking off at the end of the bench.
• Ask the children to stand at the side of the bench and step on to it with one foot, pushing down hard to take their body into the air and landing on the other side of the bench.

• Ask them to run towards and along the side of the bench and jump over it with the leg that is nearest the bench leading the jump.
   Some children will be able to run along the bench and make a high, stretched shape in the air and also make stretched shapes while jumping across the bench. Those who display this kind of ability should be encouraged to practise their skill.

Mats

Most children will jump higher and stretch themselves more if they have a mat to cushion their feet on impact at landing. The following activities will help the children to improve their skill.
• Ask one child at each mat to curl up on the floor next to the mat. Another child can then practise running and jumping over the curled-up child landing on the mat.
• Encourage the children to jump as far as possible. They should also be encouraged to practise landing with one foot after the other and with both feet together.
• Ask the children to practise jumping across the mats with two feet together followed by both feet apart.
   Encourage the children to make movement patterns on, across and around the mat. They can choose a movement pattern based on different kinds of jumps. They might like to try a rhythm, for instance, three jumps with their feet together and three jumps with their feet apart. Once they have practised the pattern ask them to try to perform the pattern backwards with a turn at different levels or at various speeds.

Large apparatus

Select apparatus from which the children can jump such as table tops, stools, padded benches and so on. (An apparatus layout is suggested on the opposite page.)
The children can then try some of the following movement tasks.

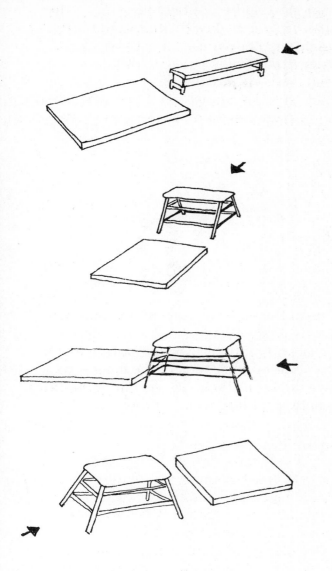

• 'Climb on to the apparatus and stretch your arms, hands, spine and legs in the air before you land safely.'

Theme: weight bearing leading to balance

This theme is intended to help focus the children's attention on the parts of their body on which they can hold their body still. The body has broad surfaces such as the back, stomach, bottom, hips and shoulders, which can be used to support its weight. Less broad surfaces such as the shins and smaller areas such as the knees and hands can also be used to support the body, but when using these areas it is much harder to keep the body still.

The aim in exploring this theme is to develop the children's control when holding their body weight on different surfaces and also to become more aware of the ease or the difficulty of supporting parts of their bodies in various circumstances.

Warm-up

• Ask the children to jog, walk, jog, walk and so on around the area.
• Ask them to walk with long stretched strides and then small steps – forwards and backwards.
• Ask the children to walk on tiptoe taking very small steps.
• Tell the children to lie on their sides and stretch, making their bodies as long as they can. Then tell them to curl up small. They should do this on their left and right sides. Can they move like a caterpillar, curling up small and then stretching out?
• Ask the children to jump around the area, keeping both feet together. They should make small jumps and then long jumps.
• Tell the children to stand still on one of their feet and hold the position while they count up to ten.

Movement tasks

You may find that many young children will not have experienced jumping from a height and will therefore need to be treated sympathetically. In particular, very young children will almost certainly need a helping hand from you during their first attempt and all the children will need to have the opportunity to try and step off the apparatus and practise their landings before being asked to jump off. The following are suggested tasks:
• 'Climb on to the apparatus and step off.' (Remind the children that they must bend their hips, knees and ankles when they land.)
• 'Climb on to the apparatus and jump off.'

Floorwork

Take the children through the following list of movement tasks so that they become aware of the concept of weight bearing.
• Ask the children to walk about the area and stand absolutely still when you say 'freeze'. Do the same again but with the children running.
• Ask them to sit on the floor and lift their legs and arms in the air and stretch.

• Ask the children to lie on their backs, lift their legs and bottoms in the air and stretch.

• Ask the children to lie on their fronts and lift their legs, chest and arms off the floor stretching into a banana shape.

• Ask them to make bridges by facing the floor and supporting their weight on both hands and feet. They should then lift each leg off the floor in turn. Tell them to try this when their backs are nearest to the floor.
• Ask the children to face the floor and make the widest star shapes possible supporting their weight on both their hands and feet.

• Ask the children to find out which other parts of their bodies they can put their weight on. Encourage them to try their shins, elbows and knees; their knees and head; and one foot.
• Ask them to choose two parts of the body to put their weight on at the same time.

• Show the children how to do shoulder stands. They should lie down on their backs and lift their legs and bottoms in the air, pointing their toes to the ceiling. Make sure they tuck their elbows into their sides and support their hips on their hands.

• Let the children practise taking their weight on to smaller, less stable bases, for example two hands and one foot leading to one hand and one foot; two knees and two elbows leading to one knee and one elbow. You can also challenge the children by asking them to find other small parts of their bodies to take their weight on.
• Ask the children to practise holding their bodies still when balancing on one foot. Tell them to make a stretched shape with the other foot, leg and both arms.
• Ask the children to make a stretched shape while standing on one foot, then the other. How long can they hold these positions?

24

• Ask the children to try making various body shapes when their body is supported first on a broad surface, then a medium surface, and then a small surface. Tell them to change the shapes slowly and quickly.
• Ask them to make a movement pattern, choosing three different parts of the body to take their weight and using other parts to move them from one place to another.

Intermediary apparatus

Mats

Having completed the floorwork, Year 2 children can be taught a headstand. Show them how to make a strong triangular base with the hair-line pressed into the mat and both hands, palms down, with the fingers facing the head. At this point the body will be in a crouch position and they should walk their feet forward, keeping their spines straight and pushing down equally on both hands and their heads. When their weight is almost totally transferred to their heads and hands, and keeping their legs bent, the children should slowly transfer all their weight to their triangular bases, pulling their hips up over their heads until they are immediately over their shoulders. They should bend their knees and gently lift their feet into an inverted tuck position and slowly straighten their legs.

Once they have completed their headstands the children should bend their knees, put both feet on the ground and return to a crouch position.

As well as a headstand the children can also try some of the following balancing exercises on their mats:
• Ask them to practise shoulder standing. What can their legs do in the air?

• Ask them to take both legs over their heads and stretch them. Can they make their toes touch the mat?

• Ask them to kneel down on one leg and stretch the other leg and both arms away from their bodies. Can they hold the position until you count to ten?

the children to each balance on one
and lean forward until their bodies
make 'T' shapes.

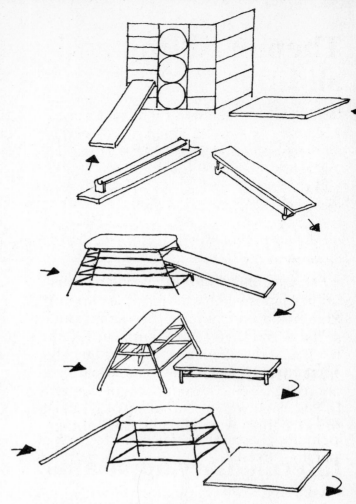

It is at this stage that children should be
able to show their ability in fulfilling the
requirements of all aspects of the Key Stage
1 attainment target. For instance, they
should be able to plan and perform safely a
range of single and linked movements in
response to given tasks and stimuli, to
practise and improve their performance
and describe what they and others are
doing and recognise the effects of physical
activity on their bodies.

In order to develop and refine the
requirements, ask the children to make a
movement pattern by choosing three parts
of their bodies to balance on and then find
interesting movements to take them from
one balance to another. Let them share the
resultant performances with their peers.

Large apparatus

Set out the apparatus as shown above.
The arrows indicate the direction of travel.
Guide the children through some of the
following movement tasks.

Movement tasks

• 'Explore the apparatus.'
• 'Choose a place on the apparatus where
you can hold your body weight on a broad
base. Use interesting movements to get on
and off the apparatus.'
• 'Choose three places on the apparatus
and three different parts of your body to
hold your body still. Link the still positions

with other movements so that you create a
pattern.'
• 'Choose a small part of your body to
balance on and hold in stillness somewhere
on the apparatus.'
• 'Choose two places on the apparatus
where you can hold your body in stillness
on a small base.'

Encourage the children to plan, practise
and refine a movement pattern and be
ready to perform it. For example, ask them
to get on to their apparatus in a novel way
and then form interesting shapes. Tell them
to hold their shapes and then find
interesting ways to move into other shapes
and hold them. They should then choose
different ways to complete their patterns.

The children should be encouraged to
extend their movement practice when they
are working on climbing frames. For
instance, some children will be able to hang
from their hands or their knees and a
percentage of children will be able to hold
their bodies in stillness on their bottoms
and the tops of their legs.

Theme: rolling and sliding

Rolling is an essential skill in gymnastics because it is a useful linking movement at all developmental stages; even Olympic gymnasts need to know how to roll! In addition many advanced skills in gymnastics depend on an ability to rotate the body on to, around, over, on, along and off pieces of equipment, and to rotate in the air and on the floor.

Rocking is a helpful pre-activity which leads into rolling and enables children to gain confidence in transferring their weight from one part of their bodies to another.

Warm-up

• Ask the children to sing 'If you're happy and you know it – clap your hands', including the commands: 'stamp your feet', 'pat your head/shoulders', 'touch your knees/toes/elbows' and so on.
• Ask them to sit on the floor and tap their toes on the ground one after the other. Then ask them to stand up and tap their toes and then their heels on the ground one after the other.
• Ask the children to jump from side to side and from one foot to the other.
• Tell them to move about the room on their hands and feet.
• Ask the children to lie on the floor and stretch fully. First they should lie on their tummies and then on their backs.
• Ask the children to stretch up high and clap their hands. Then ask them to clap their hands near their feet, far out to their right and far out to their left.
• Tell them to shake their feet one after the other and then shake their hands and shrug their shoulders up and down at the same time. Then ask them to shake both arms from the shoulders and each leg, in turn, from the hip.
• Can they touch and identify all the parts of the body which they have not yet used, such as their ears, eyes, noses and mouths?

Floorwork

When working on rolling and pre-rolling activities try to use mats wherever possible so that the children can gain more confidence. A variety of movement tasks should be presented to the children so that they can discover how the surfaces and parts of their bodies can be used. This is very useful preparation for teaching them the gymnastic skills of forward and backward rolls.
• Ask the children to stand on both their feet and practise stretching high and curling down into a tucked position.
• Ask them to jump in a crouched position on the floor around a mat. To do this they should put their weight on both their hands and then transfer the weight to both feet.
• Ask the children to lie on their backs and rock from side to side in a tucked position. They should then rock from their shoulders to their bottoms and feet, keeping their knees tucked in and trying to put their heels near to their bottoms.
• Can the children rock backwards from a sitting position? Tell them to keep their heels near their bottoms. Can they now rock forwards and finish on their feet?
• Tell the children to stretch out on their backs, and then roll across the mat. Can they keep their legs and arms off the mat?
• Ask the children to roll sideways across the mat in a tucked position.
• Tell the children to experiment pushing, pulling and sliding across the floor with and on different parts of their bodies.
• Group the children together and give each group two mats. Arrange the mats so that there is a space between them of about two metres and ask the children to roll sideways across the first mat, slide or pull themselves across the floor and roll sideways across the second mat. Encourage them to try each of the two sideways rolls and to try to find useful linking and sliding movements to take them into and out of the rolls. Remind the children to think of good starting and finishing positions, body shape and linking movements.

Backward roll

To build up the skills needed to do a backward roll the children should practise rocking from their bottoms to their shoulders. Make sure they tuck their legs in and place the palms of their hands on the floor at either side of their heads and with their elbows bent. Emphasise the rocking action towards the shoulders and the hand position as well – both palms facing forwards (thumbs near to ears).

When rocking backwards they should keep their spines rounded and their elbows bent. The palms of their hands should face

the ceiling, ready to push on to the floor at the sides of the head at the end of the rocking action. When they actually begin to do the backward roll they should start off in a crouched position, sit and roll backwards keeping a rounded spine and their legs tucked. They should put their hands on the floor, with their thumbs facing their ears and thrust and extend their arms to get their hips high. They should lift their heads quickly and put both feet on the floor, returning to the crouched position.

Forward roll

The children will need to have some knowledge of how to control their body weight, an awareness of body tension and strong arms if they are to be able to complete a *safe* forward roll. Younger children should not practise this activity without adult supervision and a useful way to make sure that all the children are supervised is to place a thick mat at one end of the room so that you can supervise the rolls, while at the same time maintaining a full view of all the children as they work on other tasks.

When teaching the children to do a safe forward roll tell them to stand off the mat with their legs spread wide. They should lean forward with their arms extended and their hands ready to take their weight.

They should tuck their heads between their legs and fall forward, pushing with their hands on to their shoulders.

Large apparatus

Set the apparatus out so that each group has a bench or plank to push, pull or slide on and a mat on which to roll sideways. The following is a suggested layout for the apparatus and can be used as a basis for the following movement tasks.

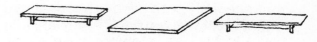

They could also begin the roll in a crouched position. From this position they should lean forwards with their arms extended until their hands touch the floor. At the same time, they should thrust their feet off the floor, tucking their heads in, rounding their spines, bending their knees, tucking their feet in near to their hips and reaching forward with their hands.

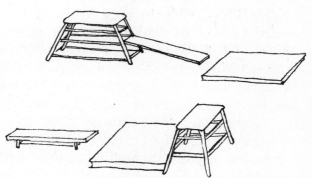

To gain the standing position after rolling, they must make sure their heels are close to their bottoms and their arms are reaching upwards and forwards.

Movement tasks

• Ask the children to explore their apparatus and show you where they can pull, push, slide and complete a sideways roll. If you have already helped the children to learn a backward roll, it will be necessary to limit this initial task to a stretched sideways roll only.
• Ask them to choose the places on the apparatus where they can push, pull, slide and roll. Remind them to think about how they can link these movements together.
• Tell each group to move to another piece of apparatus and make a new movement pattern.
• Can the children suggest ways of arranging the apparatus and explain why.

Throughout these tasks check for good body tension and clear shapes as the children push, pull, slide and roll. Help them to create linking movements.

Theme: partners

Partner work adds another dimension to gymnastic activities established in Year 2. At this stage, children become much more aware of the forces which need to be generated if they are to work simultaneously with each other as they create movement patterns. They are also much more aware of the similarities and differences between themselves and other children.

The DES document, *Mathematics in the National Curriculum* (1989) indicates that several maths concepts can be reinforced during gymnastic lessons. The theme of partners gives children an opportunity to consolidate their knowledge of spatial concepts such as 'under', 'over', 'next to', 'behind', 'in front of' and so on. 'Reflection' is another mathematical concept which can be reinforced within gymnastics. Children can be helped to understand this concept by imagining a mirror. However, before younger children can really understand, they need to work through simple practice exercises which will involve them working alongside, behind, in front of and touching a partner.

Warm-up

• Ask the children to jog around the area and 'freeze' on command.
• Ask them to skip around the area with high knee lifts.
• Tell the children to walk with their hands as high in the air as they can.
• Ask them to walk with their hands as close to the ground as they can.
• Ask the children to jog on a straight pathway, jog on the spot and then turn round and jog back to the starting place. When the children repeat this, ask them to walk on a zigzag pathway, turn round and

return on a zigzag pathway to the starting place. Finally, ask the children to use a circular pathway to leave and return to the same starting place.
• Ask the children to stand still and choose a place high above their heads and use a circular pathway and then a straight pathway to take their right, then left and finally both hands from their hips to the chosen place.
• Ask the children to put their body weight on their hands and feet and lift each foot and then each hand in turn up in the air on a straight, and then curved, pathway.

• Ask them to run as fast as they can, but warn them that they must be ready to stop suddenly when you tell them.

Floorwork

• Ask the children to face their partners and clap hands with each other. They should then hold hands and try to step *gently* on their partners' toes!

• Ask the children to stand behind their partners and follow them wherever they go.
• Tell the children to stand beside their partners and practise walking and jogging together, but constantly change direction.
• Ask one of the children in each pair to make a 'bridge' and let their partner go under, over and around their bridge.
• Ask the children to face their partners and ask one of them to pretend to be a mirror and reflect their partners' movements. They can experiment with movements at different levels and with movements which take them away from and near to their partners.
• Ask the children to join right hands and try to pull their partners towards them.
• Ask the children to sit down with their legs stretched out in front of them, making sure that the soles of their feet touch their partners' feet. They should then try to push their partners' feet away.

Intermediary apparatus

Hoops

• Ask the children to jump into a hoop at the same time as their partners. They can try jumping forwards, backwards and sideways.
• Ask the children to see whether they can jump into a space which their partners have just jumped out of!

Benches

• Ask the children to follow their partners along a bench at a slow walking pace. Can the children walk along in their partners' footsteps?
• Tell the children to practise synchronising their movements so that they step on to, step off and step over the bench together. They can then move on to try stepping on forwards, stepping off backwards and stepping on backwards and stepping off forwards together.
    Finally, the children can make up and repeat their own movement patterns.

Mats

• Ask the children to roll across a mat together in a stretched shape.

• Ask the children to roll across a mat together sideways, in a curled shape.

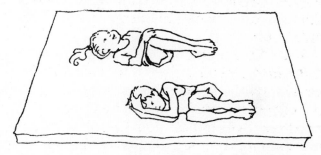

• The children can practise rotating around their hips and spines, keeping their weight on their hands and feet.

• Ask the children to make up a sequence of movements which will take them across the mat, across the floor and across the bench.

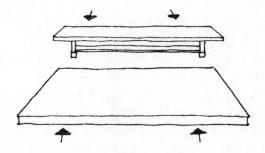

Large apparatus

Set the apparatus out as shown in the diagrams and ask the children to make a sequence of matching movements which they perform together, but starting at opposite ends.

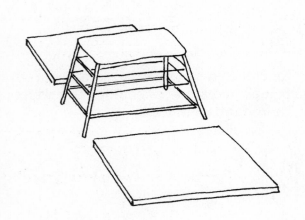

Cool-down

These ideas can be used as cool-down activities for all the themes mentioned.
• Ask the children to lie on their backs, or fronts, and stretch until all their muscles are tense. Tell them to relax like a rag doll.
• Ask the children to walk without making a sound. They must also try to keep their backs straight and their heads erect, while keeping their eyes looking forward.
• Touch parts of your body and ask the children to touch the same parts on their body. They must do this silently!
• Tell the children to sit down and stand up very slowly and smoothly.

• Ask the children to lie on their backs and lift their arms and then their legs into the air. They should then put them on the floor very quietly and slowly.
• Ask the children to sit on the floor with their backs straight and stretch out their legs bending them until their feet are close to their bottoms.
• Tell the children to close their eyes and spread their arms out and 'feel' their way round the room.
• Tell the children to sit with their arms and legs crossed and their backs straight. You should touch each child and as you do so they must follow you as you make various pathways across the floor.
• Act out rhymes with the children. There are many rhymes which provide suitable calming and cooling down activities.

As the children grow older, you may prefer to choose to build on the stretching activities such as the ones listed above. Remember that it is important in the cool-down period to reduce the level of activity and exercise slowly. Any light and easy stretching helps remove waste products from the muscles and reduces any stiffness produced by strenuous work.

Evaluation

Use the photocopiable 'tick charts' on pages 33–34 to provide a profile of each child's attainments and an overall class profile.

The first chart is structured in response to the End of Key Stage 1 Attainment Target. This table can be refined by recording the child's abilities with a score:
• 1 – reaches the required standard;
• 2 – above the required standard;
• 3 – shows outstanding ability.

The second chart is specific to the skills in the programme of study in this chapter. It will provide a more detailed profile of attainment and a more detailed analysis of achievement for your records.

Children with special needs might need a separate sheet so that you can make more detailed notes about specific problems.

Evaluation sheet
Gymnastics Key Stage 1

Name

• Plans and performs safely a range of simple actions and linked movements in response to given tasks and stimuli. Floorwork: Creative							
Good body shapes							
Uses a variety of speeds							
Links movements together							
Practises and improves performance							
Apparatus: Creative							
Good body shapes							
Uses a variety of speeds							
Links movements together							
Practises and improves performance							
• Describes what s/he and others are doing.							
• Recognises the effects of physical activity on his/her body.							

	Name							
• Other skills								
Co-operative								
Leader								
Understands instructions								
Can lift, carry and manoeuvre apparatus								
Runs, leaps and lands with control								
Can hop on each leg								
Jumps from two feet high in the air								
Can balance on large body parts								
Bunny jump								
Caterpillar walk								
Can balance on one foot for 30 seconds								
Roly-poly/sideways roll								
Sideways tucked roll								
Straddle roll								
Jump down from apparatus								
Climb confidently								
Descend confidently								
Balance on shoulders								
Forward roll								
Backward roll								
Makes different shapes in various places on the climbing frame								
Bunny jump over a bench								
Headstand								

Chapter 2
Games

'Competitive games, both individual and team, are an essential part of any programme of physical education. They are part of our national heritage and offer a range of educational opportunities. To explore to the full those opportunities it is necessary to offer pupils a balance of games experiences' (*PE for ages 5 to 16*, 1991).

'Pupils should:
• experience using a variety of games equipment, where appropriate, specially designed equipment for pupils with physical disorders;
• experience, practise and develop a variety of ways of sending, receiving and travelling with a ball;

• experience elements of games play that include chasing, dodging, avoiding and awareness of space and other players;
• be given opportunities to make up and play games with simple rules and objectives that involve one person and a limited amount of equipment extended to working with a partner when ready' (Programme of Study).

There has been a tendency in recent years for educators of young children to sacrifice the direct, systematic teaching of games activities, to an open-ended, free-choice approach. The philosophy has centred around the notion that children motivate themselves into learning situations if they can select to play with a piece of apparatus of their own choice.

However, researchers Cooper (1977) and Hutt (1972) have shown, after analysing their observational studies of children, that children's activity is much better stimulated and is performed with increased quality when an informed adult assists and co-operates in active learning. Also, Warburton and Wetton (1991) were able to demonstrate that differences in gender performances are less marked when children have equal access to a structured programme.

This chapter concentrates on a 'hierarchy of skills' approach to games activities. The skills are presented chronologically and it is assumed that they will only be attempted when the class teacher considers that her children are ready to acquire them. The material is divided into the seven developmental stages through which infant-aged school children progress as they develop physical maturity and the motor ability to start playing traditional games with others. It is important to be aware that there is often a wide range of games ability across any one class of children, which is often the result of cultural nurturing outside the school situation. For example, a small percentage of children can kick and throw balls quite competently when they are five years old while others have difficulty in even running with any confidence. Because of these disparities I would urge you to teach *all* the skills and *all* the activities to *all* the children so that everybody, including those with special needs, will have access to the whole programme.

Stage one

All children require sympathetic treatment during their first weeks in school. Many may not have any experience of working in a large space and certainly some will not have played with such a large number of children before. Stage one, therefore, is seen as an induction stage in which the children are orientated into these experiences by playing ring games and being involved in action songs and rhymes with the whole class and with their teacher. These kinds of activities will provide a useful base for learning the first four essential skills of games playing, which are:
• skill one: becoming familiar with the environment;
• skill two: building confidence and self-esteem;
• skill three: listening to instructions;
• skill four: acquiring general body management.

Suggested activities

• Sing the song 'Heads and shoulders, knees and toes' and do the actions.
• Stand with the children in a circle and sing 'The grand old Duke of York' while doing the following actions: to lines one and two march on the spot; to line three march, with knees lifted, to the centre of the circle; to line four march backwards to starting place in the circle; to line five stretch high on tiptoe; to line six crouch down; to line seven tiptoe on the spot.
• Sit with the children in a circle and sing:
   Peter taps with one hammer,
   One hammer, one hammer.
   Peter taps with one hammer
   All day long.
   While they sing, the children can make a chopping action with one of their hands. They should then sing, 'Peter taps with two hammers...' and this time make a chopping action with both hands. They can then sing, 'Peter taps with three hammers...' while chopping with two hands and banging one heel on the floor and so on.
• Try playing ring games such as 'Here we go round the mulberry bush', 'There was a princess long ago', 'Ring a ring o' roses', and 'The farmer's in his den'.

   There are many collections of rhymes and songs which you probably already use in a classroom situation to help children feel rhythms and to articulate sounds and words. Select those rhymes and songs which have a lot of action in them, such as 'I'm a little tea-pot', so that the children can practise and enjoy them in a large space.

Stage two

When the children are showing more awareness of large space environments and are more confident physically, it will be possible to start to structure the lessons to include the following essential elements:
• Warm-up: select a few activities, lasting three to five minutes in total, that increase the children's breathing and heart rates.
• Skill learning: select one skill from the chronological list to emphasise for about ten minutes of each lesson.
• Games and activity stations: involve the children in either a game or activity station which allows them to practise the skill to which they have just been introduced.
• Cool-down: give the children a quiet activity which allows a calm transition back to the classroom and the body to return to normal functioning.

When they reach this development stage it is easier, for both you and the children, if the activities selected do not require the use of apparatus. During this stage the children will have the opportunity to acquire skills five to seven while, at the same time, building on skills one to four. Skills five to seven can be acquired simultaneously over several lessons, as they are to some extent interdependent and form the basis of the simplest games:
• skill five: introduction to locomotor skills;
• skill six: movement in different directions;
• skill seven: movement at different speeds.

Warm-up

As the children will be working on locomotor skills (movements which will take their bodies across the area) exercising their lower bodies is more important than exercising their upper bodies. It would be valuable, therefore, if each warm-up concentrated on some stretching activities and some foot exercises to increase the children's general mobility before starting each lesson.
• Ask the children to stretch their arms high in the air and to circle and then shake their hands from their wrists.
• Ask the children to shake each of their feet in turn.
• Encourage the children to keep their backs straight and their heads erect, and to bend their ankles, knees and hips until their bottoms are touching their heels. They should then stand up again slowly.
• Ask the children to walk around the area on their toes.
• Tell the children to make large strides in different directions all over the area. They can stride backwards and sideways as well as forwards.

Skill learning

Encourage the children to practise the following locomotor skills in turn: walking, jogging, running, hopping, jumping, leaping, skipping. The children should also practise stopping. Ask them to walk anywhere and to stop suddenly when you call 'freeze'. They should practise all seven locomotor skills in turn and complete a sudden stop and then try the seven locomotor skills in turn while moving forwards and backwards. Ask them, 'Can you walk sideways? And while you are turning?' and so on. With your guidance, let the children experiment with the locomotor activities.

They should attempt to carry out the seven locomotor skills at normal speed and then at a faster speed and finally as fast as possible. The children will also find it fun to try and use some of the locomotor skills to move as slowly as possible.

Suggestions for games

• Play 'What's the time Mr Wolf?' where the children ask the time as they follow you around the area. Each time they ask you, make up a time in response. When you answer 'dinner time' the children must run away so that 'the wolf' cannot catch them.
• Play 'Captain's coming'. You must tell the children to pretend that they are the crew on a ship and you must call out a variety of commands to which there are set responses:
'Captain's coming!' (*Everyone salutes.*)
'Wash the decks!' (*Everyone pretends to scrub the floor.*)
'Climb the main brace!' (*Everyone mimes climbing a rope.*)
'Sharks!' (*Everyone lies on their stomachs and lifts their arms and legs off the floor.*)
'Starboard!' (*Everyone runs to the right of the room.*)
'Port!' (*Everyone runs to the left of the room.*)
'Man overboard!' (*Everyone lies down and does not move.*) The last person to lie down is out of the game.
• Play the 'Bean game'. Ask the children to jog around the area until you call out the name of a bean. The children must then stop jogging and complete the following actions:
If you call out 'jelly bean' the children must shake their arms, legs, heads and spines.
If you call out 'frozen bean' the children must stand still as if they are frozen.
If you call out 'jumping bean' the children must jump with both feet on the spot.
If you call out 'French bean' the children must kick their legs up like a can-can dancer.
If you call out 'runner bean' the children must run quickly.
If you call out 'chilli bean' the children

must jump from side to side as if the floor was too hot to stand on.
If you call out 'baked bean' the children must lie on the floor with their arms and legs stretched out as wide as they can.
• Play 'Simon says'.
• Play 'Grandmother's footsteps'. Line up all the children side by side and stand at the opposite end of the area with your back to the children. The children must then try to creep slowly towards you but if you turn round and see a child moving, that child must return to the start.

Cool-down

• Tell the children to stand up straight in a good postural position and then check their alignment.
• Ask the children to sit down with their legs crossed. They must then try to change from this position to a sitting position with their legs stretched out in front of them; they have to do this slowly and without any bumps or scrapes on the floor.
• Ask all the children to lie on the floor and try to keep perfectly still. You should then walk among them touching individual children. As you touch each child in turn they must stand up and try to walk back to the classroom as quietly as they can.

Stage three

When the children are happy and confident moving about the area using the various locomotor skills and when they can also listen and respond to instructions, they can be introduced to some apparatus. At first, only introduce them to apparatus which is easy to manipulate; for example, first bean bags and then quoits, large balls, small balls, skipping ropes and bats and balls. The children need to become comfortable with each piece of apparatus before any discrete skills can be taught and it is crucial that each child has a piece of apparatus for himself.

Stage three can be seen as an important transitional stage between activities performed without apparatus and activities performed with apparatus. One of the best pieces of apparatus to use during this transitional stage is the 'humble' bean bag! The bean bag is easy to catch, easy to manipulate, easy to manoeuvre and, as teachers of young children know only too well, it saves valuable fielding time because it doesn't roll away! During the transitional stage, and using a bean bag, the children will be able to practise skill eight: travelling with a bean bag.

Warm-up

• Ask the children to clap their hands, stamp their feet, clap their knees, clap their hips, clap their shoulders, and stamp their feet again.
• Tell the children to walk, then run, then walk, then run, as you tell them to 'change' from one to the other.
• Let the children walk around the area. As they walk they should touch the floor when you give the command 'touch'.

Skill learning

• Ask the children to try and balance the bean bags on different parts of their bodies such as their heads, chests, arms and knees. Can they find some other places on which to balance their bean bags? Can the children walk with bean bags on their heads? What about with them balanced on their chests or feet?
• Ask the children to try to walk, jog, jump and run while holding bean bags between their knees. Can they do this with the bean bags between their ankles?
• Ask the children to jump while each keeping a bean bag under one of their arms, between their knees or ankles, or under their chin.
• Ask the children to run and put their bean bags on a line and return to the start.

    Encourage the children to use both their right and left hands and both hands together where appropriate.

Suggestions for games

• Play a game of 'Simon says' using commands such as 'put the bean bag on your head', 'put the bean bag on your shoulder' and so on.
• Fill a basket or box with all the bean bags. You should then try to scatter them while the children field them and return them to the basket. The object of the game is for the children to try and stop you emptying the basket.

Cool-down

• Ask the children to sit on the floor and then call out to them the names of parts of the body. The children must touch each named part of their bodies in turn.
• Tell the children to lie down on the floor and stretch out as far as they can. Then they should join in with you as you count to ten. Once they have finished ask them to stand up quietly.

Stage four

After the children's initial introduction to working with a bean bag it should now be possible to introduce them to some of the fundamental skills of playing games using first a bean bag, then a quoit and then large balls. As each piece of apparatus is introduced to the children, the first priority is for them to become comfortable in using it. Several exploratory activities are suggested to facilitate this. Once this experimental phase has been achieved, then each new piece of apparatus can be used for specific skill learning.

    During this stage of the developmental programme, the children will be able to fulfil one of the four programmes of study for games at Key Stage 1: **'Pupils should: experience using a variety of games equipment including, where appropriate, specially designed equipment for pupils with physical disabilities.'**

During this stage the children will be able to practise the following skills:
- skill nine: passing to self;
- skill ten: throwing underarm;
- skill eleven: kicking an object;
- skill twelve: rolling a quoit;
- skill thirteen: catching a ball;
- skill fourteen: bouncing a ball.

Warm-up

- Lead the children around the area. They should copy you as you walk, jog, walk on tiptoe, walk on your heels, skip, walk with your arms high in the air and with your arms wide apart.
- Show the children how to clap their hands behind their backs and then ask them to clap their hands in front of their bodies and then behind their bodies. Can the children show you other places around their bodies where they can clap their hands, for example above their heads, behind and between their legs and so on?

Skill learning with bean bags

- Let the children practise passing bean bags from their right hands to their left hands; under their right and left legs; around their bodies; behind their ankles and behind their necks. How far and how high can they throw their bean bags?
- Ask the children to push bean bags along the ground using the toes on first one of their feet and then the other. Let them experiment using their insteps and the outsides of their feet to push with. Can they push the bean bag with their heels?
- Ask the children to put bean bags on top of their feet and send them into the air.
- Tell the children to kick their bean bags. They should each put all their weight on the leg they will not use to kick and bend the knee and swing the other leg forward. They should use the insides of their feet to kick the bean bags. See whether the children can use both their left and right feet to kick.

Suggestions for games with bean bags

Set up four activity stations, one in each corner of the working area. Divide the children into four groups and let each group have a turn at working at each station.

Activity station one: throwing underarm and aiming

Set up a basket and make sure that there are enough bean bags for the children to have one each. Ask the children to take one stride away from the basket and try to throw their bean bags into the basket. Each time they complete a successful throw they should take a step away from the basket. If they miss, they should continue to practise from the same distance until they are successful.

Activity station two: kicking

Set up a row of cones so that there is one for each child in the group and ask the children to practise kicking their bean bags so that they hit the target cones from three strides away. When they can do this reasonably well, adjust the distance so that they improve their skill.

Activity station three: underarm throwing

Place hoops on the ground, making sure that there are enough hoops and bean bags for each child in the group. Ask the children to stand three strides away from the hoops and throw their bean bags over a hoop. Adjust the distance when most of the children are completing this task successfully.

Activity station four: travelling with a bean bag

Set out a row of four cones and ask each child to take a turn to run in and out of them while holding a bean bag.

Cool-down

• Ask the children to lock the fingers of each hand together and stretch both of their arms as far in front of their bodies as they can. They should do this first with the palms of their hands facing their bodies and then with their palms facing away from their bodies. Tell the children to keep their fingers locked together and to raise their hands high above their heads.
• Ask the children to stand with good posture.

Skill learning with quoits

You should assist and observe the children in their initial skill learning. When you are satisfied that the majority of them are competent and confident using a bean bag, introduce them to a new piece of apparatus. Quoits are a good type of apparatus to progress to as they are easier to manipulate than balls, but can still be used to practise rolling skills. In using quoits a similar orientation process should be adopted to that used when introducing the bean bags. Let the children have time to handle the quoits and to travel with them before introducing specific skills.

Ask the children to:
- balance quoits on different parts of their bodies;
- walk about the area with quoits balanced on one part of their bodies;
- hold a quoit and run around the area;
- pass the quoits around their bodies;
- run around the area with quoits in their right hands and then in their left hands;
- throw the quoits as far as possible and watch them land and then collect them;
- try and throw the quoits as high in the air as they can, watch them drop to the ground and where they roll to and stop, so that they can then collect them;
- sit down and pass the quoits from their left feet to their right feet.

Once the children are confident with the initial skills necessary for handling quoits, they can progress to learning specific skills.
- Ask the children to roll the quoits away and watch them until they stop.
- Let the children roll the quoits away and see how many times they can clap their hands before they stop.
- Ask the children to roll the quoits several times, run after them and pick them up, first with their right hands, then with their left hands and finally with their feet.
- Ask the children to roll the quoits at a target.
- Ask the children to spin their quoits on the floor using one and then both hands. Can they roll the quoits and keep them rolling by tapping them with their hands?

Suggestions for games with quoits

Divide the class into four groups and set up four activity stations. Using these stations the children will be able to develop the skills to which they have previously been introduced. Each group should spend about three or four minutes on each station until they have visited all the stations.

Activity station one

Make sure there are enough hoops and quoits for each child in the group. Place the hoops on the ground and ask the children to practise throwing the quoits so that they land inside their hoop. To begin with they can use their hands, but they should also see if they can send the quoits away towards the hoops with their feet. The children should stand one step away from the hoops and if the quoits land inside the hoop they should take another step back.

Activity station two

Set out four hoops in a row so that there is enough room for the children to run around them. The children should then each take a turn to run in and out of the hoops as fast as she or he can while holding a quoit.

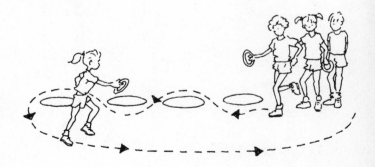

Activity station three

Set out two cones so that they are one metre apart. The children can then stand five strides away and practise rolling their quoits along the ground so that they run between the cones.

Activity station four

Set out four cones in a row ensuring that there is enough space for the children to run between them. They should then take it in turn to tap a quoit so that it continues rolling and manoeuvre it around the cones.

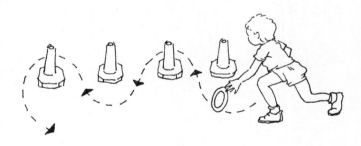

Cool-down

• Ask the children to walk about the area as slowly as they can.
• Tell the children to make themselves as 'small as a mouse' and then as 'wide as a bridge'. Can they stretch up high and make themselves as 'tall as a house' and then as 'straight as a pin'?

Skill learning with large balls

There are many new skills and experiences which children need to acquire if they are to learn the fundamental skills of game playing. It is important that every child is given the opportunity to practise with large balls such as footballs, so that they become competent enough to play team games later in life. Such practice will also make it possible for them to take part in social play both in the playground and when they are outside the school situation. Before the children attempt specific skill learning encourage them to try out the following orientation and exploratory activities.
• Ask the children to use various parts of their bodies to hold balls, for example, on the palms of their hands, under their arm-pits, between their ankles, knees, hands, wrists and feet. Working in pairs, can they hold a ball between their heads and chests?
• Ask the children to hold the balls in their right hands and pass them to their left hands and then back to their right hands again. They should then hold the balls in their left hands and pass them to their right hands and then back again to their left hands. Let the children try passing the balls around different parts of their bodies.
• Tell the children to sit down and roll the balls up and down their legs and over their bodies. They can then stand up and try to do the same again.
• Ask the children to roll the balls, and watch and chase after them. Let them do the same again, but this time ask each of them to stop the ball with one of their hands, then both hands and then one foot.
• Ask the children to throw the ball into the air and let the ball bounce on the ground. Tell them to cup both hands underneath the balls and curl their fingers around the balls, bending their elbows and bringing their hands towards their bodies.
• Show the children how to bounce a ball. Tell them to flex their arms slightly at their elbows and keeping them still, move their forearms to direct the balls downwards.

Their fingertips and thumbs should make contact with the balls and their hands and forearms should follow the balls down.

• Ask the children to try and pat the balls more than once. How many times can they do this? Ask the children to try to pat the ball with one of their hands and then the other. They can then try and bounce the balls with both hands together.

• Let the children each choose one of their hands to use to bounce the ball by patting it while walking along. Can the children walk backwards and then sideways as they bounce the balls?

Having worked through the skills described above, the children can practise the skills which they previously developed with the quoits and the bean bags:

• dribbling and kicking the balls;
• throwing the balls;
• catching the balls after a high throw and a bounce;
• running at different speeds while holding the balls.

Let the children choose which activities they would like to practise and allow them do so for a few minutes.

Suggestions for games with large balls

Activity station one

Arrange four cones in a row and ask the children to dribble the balls, using their feet, in and out of the four cones.

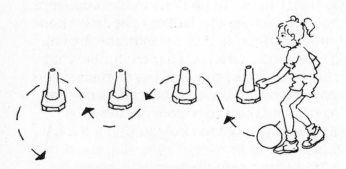

Activity station two

Place two cones a metre apart and let the children practise kicking a ball through the cones. One child can act as a goalkeeper to field the ball and return it, in turn, to the sender.

Activity station three

Arrange four cones in a row and ask the children to pat the ball around the four cones.

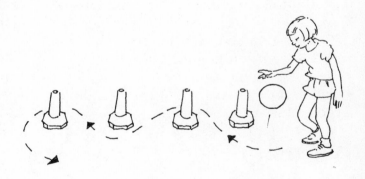

Activity station four

Place out enough hoops so that there is one for each child in the group and let them practise throwing the ball from about two metres into a hoop.

Cool-down

Say the following rhyme together and do the actions.

Scrub your dirty face (*Rub face.*)
Scrub your dirty face (*Rub face.*)
With a rub a dub dub (*Rub face.*)
And a rub a dub dub (*Rub face.*)
Scrub your dirty face. (*Rub face.*)

Other verses may include: 'dirty hands', 'dirty knees', 'dirty feet' and so on.

Stage five

By working through the preliminary activities with bean bags, quoits and large balls the children will have covered the basic games' skills. They should now be able to **'experience, practise and develop a variety of ways of sending, receiving and travelling with a ball'** (Programme of Study) by practising them with a partner. This early partner-practice is very important since it forms the rudiments of team play.

The skills to be practised are:
• skill fifteen: sending the ball;
• skill sixteen: aiming;
• skill seventeen: dribbling and stopping a large ball with the feet.

Warm-up

In this warm-up, the children will be able to **'experience elements of games play that include chasing, dodging, avoiding and awareness of space and other players'** (Programme of Study).
• Ask the children to curl up in a tucked position. They must then stretch high and curl up again and then stretch up and spread their arms wide.
• Tell the children to turn round on the spot, first one way and then the other.
• Tell the children to hop five times on their right feet and then ten times on their left feet.
• Challenge the children to hop on one of their feet and turn round on the spot.
• Let the children run round the area, but they must keep changing direction. Warn them to look for spaces and to avoid touching other people. Suggest to them that they might have to change very quickly to dodge away from or to pass another person.
• Encourage the children to run and jump high in the air and land on one of their feet after the other.
• Encourage the children to visit each corner of the area and return to where they started from without touching anyone.
• Ask the children to find a partner. When you say 'Go', one child in the pair should run away and when you say 'Partner coming' the partner must chase and try to catch her.

Skill learning

• Let each child practise rolling, kicking, bouncing and throwing a ball to his partner. Make sure that they don't stand too far apart – four strides away is about right initially – so that they are successful in completing the activities. Also continue to encourage the children to use both their left and right hands and feet when they are practising.
• Ask the children to roll, then kick a large ball between two obstacles to a partner. Then ask the children to throw the ball underarm to a partner, who should try to kick it so that it hits one of the obstacles.
• Tell the children to throw a ball underarm so that it bounces inside a hoop. Their partners should try to catch or field the balls.
• Show the children how to dribble with a ball. They should use the insteps of both their feet to tap the ball forwards and keep their knees over the balls as they tap them. To stop the balls, they should use the soles of their feet and cock their ankles, so that their feet are bent upwards and their knees are bent with the rest of their legs relaxed. Tell the children to withdraw their feet slightly at impact to cushion the ball and control it.

After practising these two associated skills the children should be allowed to practise kicking the ball to a partner. This serves the dual purpose of enabling them to practise the recently acquired skills of sending and stopping the ball as it comes towards them. Allow them a few minutes in which to choose whether to practise with their own balls or to work with a partner.

Suggestions for games

Decide whether or not to play games that require the use of apparatus and set up the appropriate activity stations. However, you may decide to play a game involving the whole class. This can be fun, especially after concentrating on specific learning.

The whole class games which follow will give children some of the experience listed in the National Curriculum documentation, for example, they will again **'experience elements of games play that include chasing, dodging, avoiding and awareness of space and other players'** and they will have the opportunity to **'play games with simple rules and objectives...'** (Programme of Study). In addition, the children will experience guided competition and learn, with sympathetic help from their teacher, the first fundamentals of working together.

Colour corners

Put a different coloured piece of apparatus in each corner of the room, for example a blue bean bag, a yellow quoit, a green ball and a red hoop. Tell the children to jog or skip around the area until you call out 'corners'. As you call, turn your back on the class until they have all chosen a corner and are standing quite still, and then call out a colour. All the children who have chosen that coloured corner must sit out until all the children are out or only one child is left in the game.

Older children can conduct the game themselves with the last child left in the game becoming the new caller.

Mouse trap

Ask half of the children to join hands and form a circle. They should hold their arms high to make arches. The rest of the class must pretend to be mice and should skip in and out of the arches and around the circle. When you call 'trap', the children holding their arms high must bring them down quickly to try and catch the mice. Mice who are caught join the circle and the last mouse to be caught is the winner.

Crumbs and crusts

Ask each child to choose a partner. Each pair should stand side by side and face you in two lines. One line should be called 'crumbs', and their partners in the other line are called 'crusts'. Call out 'crumbs' or 'crusts' and all the children in that line must turn their backs on their partners and run away. Their partners must chase after them and try to touch them before you call 'stop'. When the children have stopped ask them who managed to catch their partners. Praise the children who did and give encouragement to those who did not manage to catch anyone. Tell them to listen carefully next time and be ready to run quickly.

Butterfly touch

Let each child choose a partner. One child in the pair should stand about 15 strides away from her partner, with her back to her partner. The other child must then try to tiptoe up to his partner, touch her back very gently and then run away. The child who has been touched must turn round as soon as she feels the touch on her back and chase after, and try to catch, her partner. If the child catches her partner then the children should change places.

Busy bee

Form the children into two equal groups. One group should form a circle, and stand facing into the centre of the circle without holding hands. The other group should form another circle within the first circle facing the children in the outer circle, but about one step away. You should stand in the middle of the circles and call out various instructions for the children, such as 'shake hands', 'stand back to back', 'sit down', 'hop on the spot' and so on. When you call 'busy bee' the children in the outer circle must leave the circle and find a new partner and you too should find a partner. This means that there will be one child left without a partner and this child should take your place in the centre of the circle.

Cool-down

The activities, skill learning practices and class games listed in this section will take many weeks to complete, so a number of cool down activities are suggested. Select one or two from the list to end each lesson.
• Ask the children to stand still and close both eyes and count with you up to 20.
• Ask the children to press the palms of their hands together and then the backs of their hands together.
• Tell the children to clasp their fingers together and put the palms of their hands on their heads. Then ask them to keep their hands still and move their elbows towards each other and away from each other.

• Tell the children to stand with their feet spread so that they are shoulder width apart and press them firmly into the ground. Then without moving their feet, they should try and make both their knees meet, before returning them to their original position.
• Ask the children to stretch their right arms and hands until they are high in the air. At the same time, they should stretch their left arms so that their left hands are as near to the ground as possible.
• Ask the children to crouch down slowly and then stretch up slowly into a good standing position. They can repeat this action several times.
• Tell the children to keep their feet still and to turn at their waists until they are facing the opposite direction.
• Let the children practise circling their shoulders forwards and then backwards.
• Ask the children to walk around the area with their heads erect, their spines straight, and with a smooth walking action.

Stage six

When children reach this stage, you should be able to observe that they will have refined and developed their manual dexterity sufficiently to be able to begin to work on the motor skills associated with manipulating a small ball.

Warm-up

It is important during this stage that the children concentrate on some activities connected with loosening and manipulating their fingers, wrists and arms. By doing this, you will ensure that the children are prepared for the fine motor skill practices associated with this stage.

Begin by warming up the children's lower bodies, and giving them some experience of the element of games-play associated with 'dodging', which is one of the requirements of the National Curriculum.

Let the children walk anywhere until you tell them to 'sidestep'. They should then step to the right or left with their right or left feet leading and continue walking. Ask the children to continue walking, but this time when you tell them to sidestep they must take two steps to the right or left before continuing to walk forwards. The children can continue with this exercise, but this time they can jog and then run.

Having worked on the above, move on to concentrate on preparing the children's hands and arms for action.
• Ask the children to stretch and curl their fingers simultaneously ten times. Ensure that they stretch their fingers until no further extension is possible (until the knuckles of each hand look white).
• Tell the children to bend both arms until they can touch their shoulders. They should then bend and stretch each arm like this five times so that their palms face the floor and then five times with the backs of their hands facing the floor.
• Let the children circle their wrists clockwise and then anticlockwise.
• Tell the children to keep their arms at their sides and circle their shoulders forwards ten times and backwards ten times.
• Ask the children to circle each of their arms in turn, five times forwards and five times backwards.

Skill learning

Initially the children should have the opportunity to practise with small balls all the experimental and orientation skills they practised with the large balls. They should then also repeat with small balls the quoit and large ball activities which were suggested for skills eleven, twelve and thirteen, before they either work with a partner or begin to acquire new skills. When you are satisfied that the majority of children can manipulate and control small balls for themselves you can ask them to repeat the activities outlined for skills fourteen, fifteen and sixteen. They can also practise some additional small ball skills involving bouncing the ball on the flat of the hand, making the ball go upwards.

Give the children the opportunity **'to make up and play games with simple rules and objectives that involve one person and a limited amount of equipment'** (Programme of Study) as part of this section of stage six. Suggest starting points, for example ask the children to see how many times they can pat the ball up in the air in succession with one hand. You can discuss a scoring system, such as one point for two successive pats, two points for four successive pats and so on. You could also decide on a game structure and rules.

It is important, even when the children are making up individual games, that you encourage them to use both hands to manipulate the ball. This will help them to become reasonably ambidextrous when playing games.

From here, the children can progress to patting the ball down on to the ground and then make up a game which includes patting the ball upwards and downwards.

Finally, they can move on to practise the particular skills:
• skill eighteen: fielding a ball with the hands;
• skill nineteen: throwing overarm.

The children will have already had some experience of fielding from working on the large ball activities. They will therefore be ready to learn the correct technique for fielding a small ball. Demonstrate how to turn the body towards the incoming ball and bend down on one knee. Show how if the ball is travelling along the ground they must cup their hands curving them around the ball as it arrives, relaxing their arms to absorb the impact and pulling the ball towards themselves.

Ask the children to choose partners and practise rolling balls to each other. Ensure that each child has an opportunity to field the ball and encourage them to roll the ball to the right and to the left so that they can practise moving into the line of the incoming ball, before bending and kneeling to field it.

Throwing overarm is probably the most difficult skill to acquire. It involves quite a complicated action consisting of a combination of movements which must be co-ordinated properly if the throw is to be completed successfully. The most difficult aspect of the throw is the motion of putting the body weight behind the throw and following through with the body as the arm moves to release the ball. The children can build up to this skill by throwing from a straddled position facing a target. They should bend their arms keeping their forearms vertical and turning their bodies at the waist. At the same time they should let their arms, holding the balls, go back so that the opposite shoulders face the target. Immediately, they should straighten and thrust their throwing arms forward and release the balls. The children can use this technique to throw from a kneeling position, gradually working up to throwing from a standing position.

Suggestions for games

Activity station one

Make sure that each child has a ball and ask them to practise throwing it overarm at a wall. They should start throwing the ball from a distance of about three metres and step back one stride after each throw.

Activity station two

Ask one child to hold up a hoop at stretched arm height. Two children should then practise throwing small balls through the hoop.

The rest of the children can field the balls. Make sure that all the children take turns to throw and field the balls and hold the target.

Activity station three

Set out three skittles and ask the children to stand about seven metres away from them. They must then throw their balls and try to hit the skittles.

Activity station four

Ask the children to stand about seven strides away from their partners and practise throwing overarm to each other. Once the children have become reasonably proficient at this with a small ball ask them to try using a large ball.

Skipping

Skill twenty, skipping with a rope, is not a pure games skill, but it is nevertheless a skill which children, particularly girls, like to acquire. It is also something which girls use in their leisure and recreational time. Boys, on the other hand, are more likely to use skipping if they become interested in boxing, soccer or athletics where it is sometimes used as a fitness activity. For these reasons, therefore, it has traditionally been included in primary games programmes. There is no specific direction in the National Curriculum documentation which indicates any necessity to include this activity, but if it is included it will undoubtedly give most children enormous pleasure.

It can be legitimately included within Stage six of this programme since it can help some children to fulfill the requirement of being given **'opportunities to make up and play games with simple rules and objectives that involve one person and a limited amount of equipment'** (Programme of Study). Seven-year-old children are quite capable of making up intricate patterns associated with skipping and also of thinking up simple objectives and rules which they will apply with great diligence to any skipping game or activity.

If you are to include skipping at this stage it is a good idea to provide an additional warm-up to the ones suggested earlier for Stage 6 (see page 47). Ask the children to practise jumping on the spot with two feet together, as if they were skipping with a rope. Point out the importance of completing a rhythmic pattern, alternating a big jump with a small rebound jump.

When you start to teach the specific skill, let the children first familiarise themselves with some of the skills needed for skipping. Ask them to jump on the spot keeping their feet together. They should bend their knees and wait for a few moments after they land before doing the next jump. They can then repeat this, but this time stretching their arms out wide at either side of their bodies.

Move on to examine the skipping rope. Tell the children to hold both ends of the rope in one hand and swing it with a pendulum action. They can then hold one end of their rope in each of their hands and practise swinging it over their heads forwards and backwards. Once they have practised the basic techniques the children can put the various actions together. They should hold one end of their rope in each hand so that the rope is behind them and resting just above heel height. Then holding their hands at shoulder height they should bend their elbows and stretch their arms wide, turning the ropes over their heads in wide arcs. As the ropes touch the ground the children should jump in the air and swing the rope beneath their feet.

Give the children the opportunity to practise this skill freely. It may be a good idea to leave a rope at various activity stations so that practice is ongoing.

Cool-down

• Ask the children to turn around on the spot one way and then the other.
• Ask the children to put up their right and then their left hands and shake them.

Stage seven

Stage seven marks the transition between Key Stage 1 and Key Stage 2. Some seven-year-old children will not have refined their manipulative skills sufficiently and will not be able to achieve the motor co-ordination required to cope with using two pieces of equipment at the same time. Thus, using a bat to project a ball in a given direction and receiving and returning a moving ball with a bat are quite advanced skills for the average seven-year-old.

It is important, however, for those children who are developmentally ready, to be exposed to these skills. In addition, *all* the children should, as stated in the National Curriculum, experience a variety of games equipment. This leads the children on to skill twenty-one: batting.

Warm-up

• The children must face you throughout this activity. Ask them to jog in the direction which you call and tell them to practise moving from left to right while facing you the whole time.
• Let the children practise turning their hands quickly so that their palms face the floor and then the sky and so on.
• Ask the children to jog around the area, stopping every so often to shake hands with another child.

Skill learning

As with all new equipment, the children should have a period of time in the lesson to become familiar with the properties of the bat before they are expected to use it to propel a ball. In these first experiences, bats with two flat sides should be chosen. The size and weight of the bat can be selected from a wide variety of bat shapes. However, you should make sure that none of the different bats are too heavy for children of this age.
• Ask the children to hold the bat so that the flat part faces the floor/the sky/their right sides/their left sides.

- Ask the children to turn the bat over and over with their fingers.
- Ask the children to hold their bat firmly and face you. They should then move in the direction you call.
- Ask the children to reach high into the air with their bats and then bend down near to the ground with them.
- Ask the children to pretend to swot flies with their bats.

You may consider that it is necessary to repeat these activities in another lesson before introducing the children to the notion of batting a ball. The eye-hand co-ordination which is required to bat a ball successfully has sometimes not been acquired at this stage in children's lives and you must ensure that the children are ready to acquire this skill.

Use a bat with a short handle and tell the children to think of their bats as extensions of their fingers. When they use them with balls they must remember to keep their wrists firm.
- Ask the children to try and hold the balls on their bats and then tip them off on to the floor and pick them up again.
- Ask the children to walk around the room each with a ball balanced on their bat.
- Tell the children to put the ball on their bats, and with a forward motion, send it as far away as they can.
- Ask the children to bounce the balls with one of their hands and then use their bats to bounce the balls.

If there is a wide variety of equipment available, children could, at this time, choose to play with other types of bat such as cricket bats, hockey sticks, short tennis rackets and so on. All the sticks and bats, however, should be of the correct size and weight for children of this age.

Suggestions for games

It will not be possible to play many team games using apparatus during Key Stage 1, because the children will either not yet have acquired enough skills or will find it difficult to understand the concept of being involved in a team game. Therefore, help the children to develop their abilities progressively. Set up practice stations where the children can familiarise themselves with each piece of apparatus. This always produces an improvement in skill, but does not necessarily improve children's conceptual awareness. You should therefore consider introducing the children to small relay practices and continue with the whole class games as described earlier (see pages 46–47).

There are, however, lots of games and relays which the children can enjoy and which will also improve their skill level. If you decide to use relays it is advisable to make sure that teams consist of a maximum of four children, so that each child is active for most of the time.

Relays

- Ask the children to line up one behind the other in teams of four. The first child in the row should pass a ball, without turning round, over her head to the next child. When the last child in the row receives the ball he must run to the front of his team and continue passing the ball until the first child is once again in the starting position.

The game can also be played by passing the ball underneath their legs.

Hunter and his dogs

Choose one child to be a 'hunter' and three to be 'dogs'. They must then position themselves in the centre of the area. The rest of the children should try to run across the area to the other side, but if they are caught by the 'hunter' or his 'dogs' then they too become 'dogs'. The last child to be caught becomes the 'hunter' and can choose her three 'dogs' for the next game.

Fishes

Ask the class to form a circle and name each child in turn 'cod, haddock, salmon'. Call out one of the fish names, for example 'cod', all the children named 'cod' must run clockwise around the circle and return to their own places as fast as they can. The first child back is the winner.

• Ask each group of children to stand in a row. The first child holds a ball and runs with it around a hoop placed at the front of the line to the back of the team and gives the ball to the child at the back of the line who then passes it on to the next child and so on until it reaches the child at the head of the line and the process is repeated.

Treasure

Put a pile of bean bags at your feet and turn your back on the children. The children should then try and creep up to collect a bean bag without you noticing them. You should turn around if you hear a sound. You should place the bean bags slightly higher if there are wheelchair users in the class.

Charlie over the water

Ask the children to join hands and form a circle. Choose one child to be 'Charlie' and ask her to stand in the middle of the circle holding a large ball. The rest of the children should skip around the circle singing:

• Ask three children to line up with a fourth child facing them. This child must then pass a ball to the first child in the line who then returns the ball. As soon as he has returned the throw he must run to the back of the team and the process begins again.

Stick in the mud

Choose four or five children to be the 'catchers'. All the other children run around the area, trying to avoid the catchers. If a catcher touches someone then that person must stand still. The last four children to be touched become the catchers in the next game.

    Charlie over the water
    Charlie over the sea
    Charlie caught a blackbird
    But he won't catch me!
    On the word 'me', the children should drop hands and run anywhere in the room. At the same time, 'Charlie' must throw the ball in the air, let it drop and catch it. As she catches it she must shout 'stop!' and the children must stand where they are. 'Charlie' can then roll the ball towards a

child and if it touches him then he becomes 'Charlie'. If 'Charlie' misses she must be 'Charlie' again.

Circles

Ask the children to form groups of six and make circles. Number the children in each circle from one to six and then begin the game. The first child in each circle must run around his circle and back to his place. As soon as he is back in his place he must touch the second child who runs around the circle and back to her place. The second child then touches the third child and so on. Once all the children in the circle have run round they must raise their hands and the game has ended. The circle who raise their hands first are the winners.

Cool-down

• Ask the children to stand and face you and then pivot to face each wall of the hall in turn or, if working outside, they should turn to face north, south, east and west.
• Tell the children to stand still and stretch both of their arms in front of their bodies as far as possible without moving their feet. They must then stretch both arms behind

their bodies as far as they can.
• Tell the children to face you and, keeping their left feet and the left sides of their bodies still, stretch across their bodies with their right feet and right arms. They should then reverse the procedure on the other side of their bodies.

Assessment

'All children are entitled to have their attainment assessed in a way which will guide their future learning, progress and achievement' (*PE for ages 5 to 16*, 1991).

The statutory framework only sets down the minimum which children should achieve. This allows flexibility in the physical education programme, but good practice will involve more continuous and detailed assessment than this.
The evaluation sheet which follows is intended to assist with recording the evidence of observation of each child's performance throughout the year. It can be completed at the end of Key Stage 1 and will be particularly helpful when deciding upon the criteria which the school will expect their children to achieve. In addition these charts will allow the teacher who will be responsible for the children as they enter the second stage of their primary school education to maintain continuity and avoid the repetition of learning skills already attained.

The evaluation sheet is in the form of a simple tick list. There is, however, an additional column which can be used for comments. Children with special needs should have a separate sheet so that you can note any special achievements, problems or any strategies which have proved particularly successful. Teachers might like to consider grading their assessments as described on page 32.

Evaluation sheet
Games Key Stage 1

	Name					Comments
Helpful						
Takes turns						
Leader						
Exhibits stamina						
Exhibits locomotor skills						
Throws underarm						
Throw accuracy						
Catch a large ball – self						
Catch small ball – self						
Catch from partner						
Throw overarm						
Field a ball						
Pat bounce a ball – hand						
Pat bounce – bat						
Kick						
Kick accuracy						
Dribble ball – feet						
Skip with rope						

Chapter 3
Athletic activities

'Athletic activities concern the pursuit of the fulfilment of individual potential. Pupils strive to improve performance against measurements and/or others in maximising their performance in terms of time, height, length or distance. Athletic activities build on children's natural capacities to run, jump and throw. They promote all-round physical development – speed, strength, stamina and flexibility'
(*PE for ages 5 to 16*, 1991).

The programme of study for Key Stage 1 states that: **'Pupils should experience and be encouraged to take part in running, jumping and throwing activities, concentrating on accuracy, speed, height, length and distance'.**

This is the first time that athletic activities have been included as a *discrete* subject area within the curriculum for primary children in the Key Stage 1 age group. This chapter is therefore constructed to assists class teachers in their initial induction to teaching athletics to young children. The chapter is divided into ten distinct lessons which form, in total, the equivalent of one term's unit. They can be offered, with minor adjustments, to each of the three age groups each year. The ten lessons have all been field tested in infant schools and were well received by both the children and their class teachers.

The lessons sequentially introduce the children to the three basic skills of running, jumping and throwing. Each of the lessons can, of course, be repeated if necessary and although some of the activities in the skill practice sections may be omitted for reception class children, the overall lesson structure should be followed. Each lesson is divided into five parts:
• a warm-up: consisting of a series of activities which increase the children's heart rates, expand their lungs and extend and flex their joints and muscles so that their bodies are ready for action;
• skill practice: where the children are directed in specific skill learning;
• strength activity: which enables the children to work specifically on strengthening their muscles;
• games or athletic events: in which, initially, the children play a game which includes one or more of the three basic athletic skills and which build up to include the opportunity to practise running races and measuring throws and jumps;
• cool-down: where the children participate in a quiet activity to allow their bodies to return to normal functioning.

Lesson one: throwing underarm and broad jumping

Warm-up

• Play a game of 'Follow-my-leader'. Lead the children in a line, one behind the other. Change the pace as you move about the area; jogging, walking, skipping, walking with long strides, running and so on.
• Play 'Simon says' in the traditional manner, but choose actions which will help to warm up the children's joints and muscles; for example, 'Simon says, circle your right arm, now your left arm', 'jump on the spot', 'swing your arms', 'hop on your left leg, now your right leg' and so on.

Skill practice

Throwing underarm

The children should be shown how to throw a bean bag underarm at a target.

When directing the children to throw underarm tell them to focus on the target. They should keep their throwing arms straight as they are swung back to initiate the throw. At this stage the body weight should be placed on the back foot (the right foot for right-handed throwers). As they swing their throwing hands they should try to keep them straight and in line with the target.

The children should keep their front knees bent to receive the body weight and to help drive the body weight forward as the bean bags are released. They should try to release the bean bags when their throwing arms are at shoulder height and to follow through the throws by stepping forward with their back legs.

Once you have demonstrated this technique, divide the class into groups of four and let the children practise throwing their bean bags towards a target such as a skittle or a box.

Broad jumping

To prepare for broad jumping ask the children to jump on the spot keeping both of their feet together. Stress the importance of pushing off from their heels on to their toes at take-off and tell them to see how high into the air they can reach with their bodies. They should then jump around the room in this way, in any direction.

Once they have practised this, ask each child to collect a hoop and place it in a space. They can then practise jumping in and out of the hoops and around the hoops in the same way. Eventually, let the children try and jump over their hoops, starting and finishing with both feet together.

Strength activity

Ask the children to find a partner and shake hands with them. Then, keeping a firm grip, each child should try and pull his partner away from her chosen position.

Game

Ask the children to play the game 'Crumbs and crusts' (see page 46).

Cool-down

Ask the children to walk around the area in any direction. Encourage them to maintain good posture and walk as quietly as they can.

Lesson two: throwing underarm and broad jumping

Warm-up

• Play a game of 'Simon says', as described in the previous lesson (see page 56).
• Ask the children to jog around the area and when you call out the name of a body part or two body parts the children should put their weight on that part or parts, for example bottoms, backs, right feet, knees and so on. Then, on another signal, they should continue jogging.

Skill practice
Throwing underarm

Start this part of the lesson by allowing the children to practise throwing their bean bags freely. Remind them about the teaching points which were introduced in the first lesson. They can then practise throwing their bean bags into a hoop. Ask the children to stand about two metres away from the hoop. The distance can be adjusted as the children improve their performance. You can also encourage the children to throw for distance by challenging them to throw their bean bags over the hoop.

Broad jumping

Ask the children to spread their hoops across the area. Encourage them to run freely in the space around the hoops and then remind them how to jump into the air using both feet to launch from and land on. Ask the children to run freely in the spaces around the hoops, but whenever they reach an empty hoop to jump into it and out of it without turning, and then continue to run to the next free hoop.

Show the children how to prepare for making a broad jump from a standing position by asking them to bend their knees and swing both arms forward from behind their bodies.

The children can then continue running around and jumping in and out of their hoops, but this time they should thrust their arms forwards and upwards as they jump.

Strength activity

Ask the children to put their hands flat on to the floor. They should then place their body weight on to their flat hands, keeping their arms straight. Tell them to kick first one leg and then the other leg off the ground as if they were a kicking donkey!

Game

Arrange the children into mixed teams of four. Place a hoop about 10m away from each team and ask the children to take turns to run up to and around their hoops and then back to their teams. The first team to complete this relay are the winners.

Cool-down

Leave the hoops as they were left after the relay race and ask the children to walk behind you and lead them around the hoops. The last child in the line can pick up the hoops and put them away.

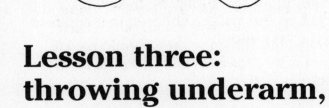

Lesson three: throwing underarm, broad jumping and sprinting

Warm-up

Ask the children to play the 'Bean game' (see page 38).

Skill practice

Throwing underarm

Allow the children to throw their bean bags underarm. They can throw them anywhere in the area and you should help individual children improve their skill where necessary.

The children should also practise throwing their bean bags so that they land inside a hoop and then, as in the previous lesson, over and beyond the hoop.

Broad jumping

Move on to practising broad jumps. Ask the children to jump around the area using both feet together and then hop on the spot, using first their left and then their right legs. Can they hop around the area, using first one leg and then the other?

Sprinting

Encourage the children to practise sprinting. Set out two markers 15m apart and ask the children to run across the area between the two.

When they run, encourage the children to lean forward and bend and swing their arms. The children can practise this action while standing still before they try it when running. Also, as the children run, encourage them to drive their arms forward and lift their knees high, making long strides. Make sure that the children run on the balls of their feet rather than flat-footed. Allow the children plenty of time in which to practise the whole action.

Strength activity

Let the children practise the caterpillar walk (see page 18).

Game

Play 'Crumbs and crusts' (see page 46).

Cool-down

Ask the children to walk in any direction until you tell them to 'freeze'. On this command they must stand as still as they can. Repeat this activity several times.

Lesson four: the three basic skills

The children will need two sessions in order to complete all the material which is presented in this lesson.

Warm-up

• Ask the children to 'jog' or to 'walk' when they hear the command to do so. Repeat the commands alternately.
• Tell the children to stand with their arms stretched out wide and their feet spread so that they are shoulder width apart. They should swing their straight arms forwards until they touch and then backwards as far as possible to touch behind their backs.

Tell the children to keep the same position, but this time they should turn at their waists so that their straight arms move alternately to the front and to the back of their bodies.
• Encourage the children to stride around

the area making the longest strides they can manage.

Skill practice

Throwing underarm

Group the children into teams of three. Each child in the team should collect a hoop and place them in a line so that they are about 3m, 5m and 7m away from the team. (Adjust the distances of the hoops according to the children's abilities.) The children can then take it in turns to throw a bean bag, aiming into the furthest hoop they can reach accurately.

Broad jumping

Leave the hoops in the same position as required for the underarm throwing practice and ask the children to stand next to the first hoop.

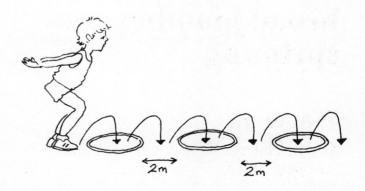

They should then take it in turns to practise jumping into and out of and over each hoop, keeping both feet together.

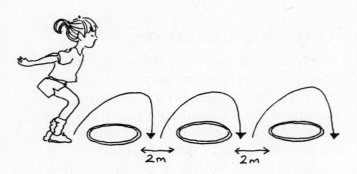

Sprinting

Let the children take turns to sprint around all three hoops and return back to their places. Use this opportunity to reteach the sprinting technique outlined in the third lesson.

All these activities can be repeated as often as time allows.

Strength activity

Ask the children to do bunny jumps. They should crouch down and place all their weight on their feet and then transfer all their weight to their hands, tucking in their legs while in the air.

Game

Ask the children to play 'Stick in the mud' (see page 52).

Cool-down

Get the children to crouch down near to the ground and uncurl very slowly until they are in a standing position. They should then curl up again very slowly until they have returned to the crouched position.

Lesson five: throwing overarm, leg strengthening and the standing start

This lesson is intended for the older children in Key Stage 1 and, because of the nature of the content of the lesson, should be taught indoors.

Warm-up

Ask the children to perform the following tasks:
• jog anywhere in the room until they hear the word 'change' and then turn and jog in another direction;
• move about the room using long, stretched strides in any direction;
• skip about the room lifting their knees high one after the other.

Skill practice
Throwing overarm

Tell the children to sit in a straddle position facing a partner. Each child should take a turn at throwing a bean bag, using an overarm throw, so that it hits her partner's chest.

The children should then be asked to stand up and be directed to hold the bean bags in the palms of their hands and squeeze them with all their fingers. They should bend their arms so that their forearms are vertical, and their fingertips facing the ceiling. They should then turn their bodies at the hips and rotate as far to the right (for right-handed children) or left (for left-handed children) as possible. As they turn, they must bend their throwing arms and let them go back. They should thrust their arms forward from their shoulders as their bodies return to their starting positions and straighten their arms. Tell the children to look at their partners' chests as they release the bean bags.

Leg strengthening

To work on the leg strengthening activities the children will need to work on a bench in groups of four.
• Ask the children to walk along the bench and jump off the end, landing on two feet.
• Ask them to step on to the bench from the side and jump off, landing on to two feet on the other side of the bench.
• Encourage the children to jump along the bench using two feet and jump off the end of the bench landing on two feet.
• Can the children stand at the side of the bench and jump over it? (Some children might prefer to continue to step on to the bench before trying this.)

The standing start

Let the children remain in their groups of four and practise sprinting. Tell them to

take it in turns to sprint down the length of the hall and choose some children to demonstrate their sprinting action to the

rest of the class. Use this as an opportunity to highlight the teaching points given in lesson three.

Move on to look at the standing start. Explain to the children that on the word 'set' the runner must stand so that the tip of one foot is just touching the start line. He should put his body weight on this foot and bend his knee.

The child's other leg and foot should be flexed and positioned slightly behind and to the side of the front foot. He should lean forward slightly with his arms bent, one arm in front of the body (opposite arm to leg) and one arm behind the body ready to drive forward. On the word 'go' the runner should drive off his front foot and thrust forward the leg and arm which were behind the body.

When they run tell the children to look forward and along their line of travel, driving alternately with their arms as they sprint towards the finishing line.

Strength activity

For this activity the children should pretend to be cats lapping at a saucer of milk. They should kneel down on their lower legs, placing their palms flat on the floor and keeping their arms straight. It is important to stress that they put most of their body weight on to their arms and in order 'to lap the milk' the children should bend their arms, and keeping their backs straight, gently lower their chins to the ground and pretend to lick the milk from a saucer.

The children should repeat this process about five times, depending on their age and ability.

Game

Organise the children into teams of four and let each team place a hoop about 10m away.

The children must then sprint up to their hoops, put their bean bags into them and return to stand at the back of their teams.

Once all the children in the team have left their bean bags in the hoop, they should take turns to sprint back to the hoop and collect their bean bags running back to take their place at the back of the line.

Cool-down

Ask the children to lie down on the floor and stretch out into a long shape. Then ask them to curl up slowly into a ball shape and then stretch out slowly again. They should repeat this several times.

Lesson six: the three basic skills

Warm-up

• Play the 'Bean game' (see page 38).
• Ask the children to circle their arms in turn, from their shoulders.
• Encourage the children to spread and clench their fingers.
• Ask the children to circle their wrists clockwise and then anticlockwise.
• Tell the children to hop on their left feet and then on their right feet.

Skill practice

Throwing overarm

Give the children some time to practise throwing underarm. Try to provide something for them to aim at, even if it is only a painted line on the playground.

The children can then practise throwing overarm. A right-handed thrower should stand sideways with her left shoulder facing the direction in which she wishes to throw her bean bag. She should spread her legs so that they are about shoulder width apart and place her body weight on her back (right) foot. She should then lean back slightly and bend her throwing arm. When the throw is initiated it is important that she steps forward and adjusts her body weight to her front (left) foot, as her arm drives forward and her body moves into the throw, simultaneously releasing the bean bag from a straight arm.

Let the children try the throwing action several times. You should observe their throws and pick out any teaching points which you feel need to be emphasised. Again try to give the children a target to throw at as this helps them to throw further and on a straighter trajectory.

Sprinting

Let the children practise running in a straight line. They should each put a bean bag on the ground about 10m away, and directly opposite themselves. They can use this as a guide to show them where to run. As they practise, it is important to emphasise that they do a proper standing start each time (see lesson five on page 61).

How fast can they run? Time them as, for example, they run across the playground.

Broad jumping

Tell the children to prepare for their jump by placing both feet next to the start line so that their big toes just touch it. They should practise swinging their arms backwards and forwards and bending their knees. When they jump they should thrust their arms forward, straighten their legs and drive both feet off the ground.

Strength activity

Ask the children to sit on the floor with their knees bent and their body weight evenly distributed between their hands and feet. On the command 'bottoms up!' the children should push down hard on both hands and both feet and lift their bottoms high and away from the floor.

Games

Divide the children into teams of four and place a bean bag about 10m away from each team.

The children should then line up in their teams and the first child in each team should sprint up to the bean bags and turn to face the next children. The second child in each team must then sprint up to the bean bags and stand behind the first children. They should continue until the whole team is lined up behind the bean bag.

Cool-down

Ask the children to walk quietly behind you as you make pathways: straight, curved, zigzag or circular.

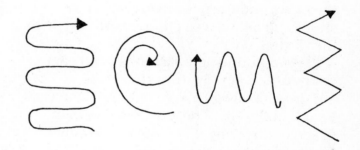

Lessons seven and eight: the three basic skills

Lessons seven and eight are identical. They are designed to enable each child to practise the three basic skills of running, jumping and throwing. The lesson structure is devised so that you will be able to help individual children while they practise the three skills.

Warm-up

• Play 'Simon says' ensuring that you choose actions which will warm up the children's arms, legs, trunks and hands.

• Ask the children to jog, walk and run alternately as fast as they can.

• Use a whistle to familiarise the children with the skill of listening to a sharp sound. They will need this skill for Lessons nine and ten where the whistle will be used to indicate the start of the sprinting races. A useful way to practise this is to ask the children to hop on one leg and when they hear the whistle to change to jumping on two feet.

Skill practice

Together with the children, set up four activity stations, one in each corner of the area.

Activity station one

At this station the children should practise throwing underarm or overarm. They should be allowed to choose which type of throw they use.

Place a hoop some distance from each child (about 4m for reception class children; 6m away for Year 1 and 7.5m for Year 2 children). The children can then practise throwing bean bags into their hoops. Encourage the children who are successful at this to throw their bean bags over their hoops.

Activity station two

The children should take turns to practise broad jumps from a standing position at this station. Either use chalk or a skipping rope to mark where the children should jump from and record how far each child can jump. It is important that this practice takes place on a grassy surface or mats.

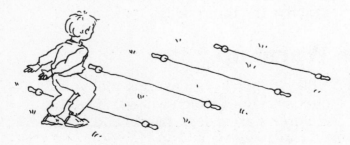

Activity station three

At this station the children can practise throwing overarm at a target.

Draw a chalk line or place a skipping rope along the ground to mark where the children should stand to make their throw. The children should then place a skittle at an appropriate distance from the line (about 4m for reception class children, 6m for Year 1 and 7.5m for Year 2 children). The children should then try to hit their skittles with their bean bags.

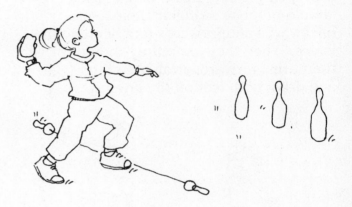

Activity station four

The children can practise sprinting at this activity station.

With the children, measure a distance of 30m and mark the distance with a skipping rope or a chalk line at one end and skittles at the other. The children should then practise running across the 30m distance in pairs. Another child can be the starter and give the three commands, 'On your marks, get set, go!'

Strength activity

Ask the children to practise bunny jumps along the ground (see page 60).

Cool-down

Touch different parts of your body and ask the children to copy you. The children must try not to make a sound while doing this.

Lessons nine and ten: measuring performance

These two lessons are the culmination of the work which the children will have completed over the term. A table showing the national average performances for the three basic skills is shown below should you require it. If you decide to measure the children's performances you will need two lessons in which to carry out the tasks.

Warm-up

Use these warm-ups for both lessons:
• Use your whistle to signal a change from walking to jogging, jogging to running, long strides to short steps, hopping on one foot to jumping on two feet.
• Ask the children to swing each of their arms in a wide circle from their shoulders. Make sure that they swing them forwards and backwards.
• Let the children jump around the area.
• Ask the children to find a space and stand in it with their legs spread shoulder width apart and their arms stretched out wide. They should then practise turning their bodies to the left and to the right.

Measuring the children's performance

Sprinting

Together with the children, measure out and mark a distance of 35m.

Arrange the children into pairs and line each pair up ready to practise running over the marked distance. Show the children where they have to run to and tell them to focus on the markers at the end of the race the whole time they are running.

Stand at the starting line and set each pair off by saying 'On your marks, set' and then blowing your whistle.

Average scores of performance					
Age at time of test		4 yrs to 4yrs 11mths	5yrs to 5yrs 11mths	6yrs to 6yrs 11 mths	7yrs to 7yrs 11mths
Sprint 35 metres	Mean	9.95 secs	9.32 secs	8.45 secs	7.86 secs
	No. of children	(187)	(1026)	(1307)	(1482)
Jump Standing start	Mean	77.83 cm	89.37 cm	103.14 cm	113.01 cm
	No. of children	(280)	(1108)	(1504)	(1721)
Throw Bean-bag	Mean	496.50 cm	570.66 cm	710.90 cm	811.15 cm
	No. of children	(280)	(1137)	(1444)	(1627)

Adapted from *Child Education* No.11 (November 1988)

After a few practice turns the children will be ready to be timed. It is useful if a parent can help at this stage, so that one adult can be present at both ends of the race. Ask two children to hold a line of wool across the finishing line.

The standing broad jump

Place a skipping rope on the grass to mark from where the children should jump. Place three skipping ropes at the following distances from the starting line:

Reception class	66cm	77cm	90cm
Year 1	77cm	90cm	110cm
Year 2	90cm	110cm	120cm

Encourage the children to see how many of the skipping ropes they can jump over.

Throwing

Provide the children with a line from which to throw and let them have a few practice attempts before measuring their throws.

If another adult can assist, each of you should take one end of the measuring tape and measure the throws instantly. If you cannot find someone else to help you, then you can put a marker, such as a garden peg, down with the child's name on it and then once all the children have had their throws you can ask them to help with the measuring and recording.

If you decide to carry out measurement of both the jumps and the throws in the same lesson you should add an active game between the events since the children will, for the most part, have been static during the measuring procedures.

Strength activity

Ask the children to put their weight on their hands and feet and make a bridge. Can they make a bridge using only one hand and one foot?

Cool-down

• Ask the children to work with their running partner. One child should be the leader and move about the area while his partner copies him. The children can take turns to be the leader.
• Invite the children to gather round and give each other a big clap for their achievements.

Chapter 4
Dance

'Dance is a distinct art form, with its own history, body of knowledge, aesthetic values, cultural contexts and artistic products. It offers a variety of learning opportunities and enables participants to enjoy physical experiences as well as develop intellectual sensibilities...' (*National Curriculum Physical Education Working Group Interim Report*, 1991).

'Pupils should:
• **experience and develop control, co-ordination, balance, poise and elevation in basic actions including travelling, jumping, turning, gesture and stillness;**
• **experience contrasts of speed, tension, continuity, shape, size, direction and level and describe what they have done;**
• **experience working with a range and variety of contrasting stimuli, including music;**
• **be given opportunities to explore moods and feelings through spontaneous responses and through structured tasks;**

• **be helped to develop rhythmic responses;**
• **experience, and be guided towards, making dances with clear beginnings, middles and ends'** (Programme of Study).

During the first few weeks in school, children's initial dance experiences will undoubtedly be influenced by and shared with other curriculum areas. Elements of music, movement, mathematics and English may all combine to awaken the children's intellectual and rhythmic senses. Most importantly, this combined activity forms a rich and firm foundation on which to develop whole body and locomotor movement responses. Familiarity with each other, the class teacher, the classroom and the school environment as a whole, will help them to gain the confidence needed to express themselves in dance situations, particularly when the children are required to work in a larger space such as the school hall. A good way of helping them to orientate themselves within the school hall, is for them to participate in some familiar action songs and rhymes. It is also useful to introduce the children to ring games. Some of these activities may overlap and can be used in conjunction with dance at this early stage of development.

Use your voice as a stimulus for action when introducing children to dance. It is much easier at this stage for them to respond to their class teacher than to music. The language you use, the tones and inflections, will help the children to feel more confident and secure as they move in a larger space.

Dance takes many forms in infant schools and children should be exposed to as many as possible from creative dance to folk and country dance. Dance is a medium which can be used to help children's aesthetic development. It gives them a chance to *feel* a rhythm or a mood as they move to a piece of music, poem, or a drum beat. Through dance children can, with careful musical selection, come to understand the moods and rhythms of other cultures.

Teachers vary in their enthusiasm to teach dance and many thousands of teachers have been grateful for the support of the BBC in producing two weekly radio programmes concerned with dance, *Let's Move* for five-year-olds and *Time to Move* for six- to seven-year-olds. However, there is no doubt that when teachers create, teach and develop their own materials, these produce much better results. They provide an opportunity to reinforce and extend the work which has been explored in the classroom. There is also much more spontaneity and excitement when classroom happenings can be instantly translated into movement experiences.

Dance and language development

Language is acquired with usage, and dance lessons offer a stimulating environment together with wide opportunities for language development.

Children, especially ones for whom English is a second language, can talk about action concepts, such as touch and jump, and can experience the action physically at the same time. You can talk to them about spatial and directional concepts while they physically carry out the task. As the children's vocabulary increases they may also develop an ability to vocalise their own feelings.

Language can also play an important part in helping children to improve the quality of their movements. Some of this language will be fundamental; for example, locomotor action words such as skip and hop, and non-locomotor action words such as twist, turn, bend and stretch. Some of the language will be expressive; for example, locomotor expressive words such as stamp, slither and scurry, and non-locomotor expressive words such as reach, screw, explode and crouch. There is also a vast bank of descriptive language which when spoken expressively, emphasising certain syllables and varying the pitch, can help the children to *feel* a movement and add quality to its execution. For example, 'The willow's branches bend and sway in the warm breeze' said in soft, quiet tones with a prolonged delivery; and, 'The tree was suddenly bitten by a sharp, crisp, cold, freezing frost' said in quick, sharp tones, emphasising the sharp sounding letters.

Moving to rhythm

A movement response can also be enhanced if the children learn a simple rhyme which they can say as they move. The words, when said in conjunction with the movements, will help the children to *feel* the rhythm, for example:
• I can jump, jump, jump.
  I can hop, hop, hop.
  Watch me, watch me
  See me stop.
• Sally is a painter.
  Stir, stir, stir.
  Likes to brush the paint on
  Whir, whir, whir.

The children should be encouraged to clap or tap their feet to the rhythm as they say the rhymes. You might like to suggest that they make up their own verses and then try them out in the hall.

Reception class children will also enjoy moving to some well-known nursery rhymes such as: 'Hickory dickory dock'; 'Pussycat, pussycat, where have you been?'; 'Cock-a-doodle do'; 'A sailor went to sea, sea, sea', and 'Incy wincy spider'. The following is an example of a lesson in which rhythm is used as a stimulation for movement.

Warm-up

Alternate beating a drum and shaking a tambourine. When the children hear the drum they should walk and run alternately. When they hear the tambourine they must stand on the spot and shake each part of their bodies.

Skill practice

• Ask the children to clap their hands to the rhyme 'One, two, buckle my shoe'.
• Ask them to sit on the floor and do the following action rhyme:

One potato (*Curl up one hand to make a fist.*)
Two potato (*Curl up the other hand into a fist.*)
Three potato (*Curl up the toes on one foot.*)
Four potato (*Curl up the toes on the other foot.*)
Five potato (*Bend both knees and tuck them into their bodies.*)
Six potato (*Put their heads on their knees.*)
Seven potato more. (*Pretend to explode stretching their arms.*)

• Let the children stand up and practise hopping and jumping to the rhythm of the following rhyme:

A sailor went to sea, sea, sea (*Hop on their left legs.*)
To see what he could see, see, see (*Jump with two feet together.*)

And all that he could see, see, see (*Hop on their right legs.*)
Was the bottom of the deep blue sea, sea, sea. (*Jump with two feet together.*)

• Let the children practise bending movements. They can start by moving their heads, working to the following rhyme:

The clock ticks (*Slowly drop their heads to their left shoulders.*)
The clock tocks (*Slowly drop their heads to their right shoulders.*)
The clock tocks (*Slowly drop their heads to their left shoulders.*)
This way (*Drop their heads to their right.*)
That way (*Drop their heads to the left.*)
And never stops.
Tick-tock (*Drop their heads to the right on tick, and to the left on tock.*)
Tick-tock. (*Drop their heads to the right on tick, and to the left on tock.*)

You can then repeat the rhyme, but this time the children can twist at the waist.

...ce

...children to create a spider dance
...the rhyme 'Incy Wincy Spider'. Show the
children a picture of a spider and let them
practise bending movements with their
arms and legs, with their hands and feet
turned out at right angles to their bodies.
• Play a piece of music, for example
'Coming round again' by Carly Simon, and
let the children move freely to the song.

Cool-down

Use particularly descriptive instructions to
calm the children and stimulate expression,
for example:
• tell them to walk silently and smoothly
around the hall;
• ask them to lift their arms gently and
spread them wide, relax their wrists and
feel as if their arms are floating.

Movement to stories

Another useful method of stimulating
movement and encouraging children to
become more aesthetically aware is to use
familiar stories. It is important however, if
children are going to produce movement of
quality, that the chosen characters and
their likely movements are analysed and
practised individually before the whole
story is explored. The following example of
a lesson shows how a story can be used in
this way.

Preparation

Before the lesson, retell the story of the
'Three little pigs'.

Warm-up

• Ask the children to stretch high, and then
to crouch down low.
• Tell them to stamp their feet four times.
• Encourage the children to lift each elbow
high and then lift each knee, their noses,
stomachs and bottoms.

Skill practice

Let the children use percussion
instruments, or their own voice sounds, as
stimuli for movement. Ask them to pretend
to be pigs. They should:
• practise wiggling their noses and tails;
• practise walking on tiptoe;
• pretend to scoop up straw with wide
sweeps of their arms;
• pretend to put the straw up high;
• practise trotting around the room;
• pretend to chop wood, using strong,
direct movements;
• pretend to carry heavy bricks.
    Ask the children to pretend to be the
wolf. Ask them to:
• walk stealthily on their hands and feet;
• walk on their 'hind legs' and hold their
paws high;
• examine their sharp, craggy, claws and
move them around their bodies;
• show their twisted faces and sharp teeth;
• look from side to side with quick, sudden
head movements;
• practise pouncing from their hind legs to
their front legs;
• practise huffing and puffing;
• practise stomping around the room;
• drive their feet strongly into the ground
and take big strides.

Dance

As you tell the children the story of the
'Three little pigs', ask them to follow the
story by making the appropriate
movements and actions. Help them to be
expressive and make good quality
movements by using descriptive language;
for example:
    The crafty wolf stalked the little pigs
    taking long, smooth strides. He kept his
    nose near to the floor. He had sharp,
    spiky claws and his face was twisted. He
    prowled around, moving his head from
    side to side with sudden movements. His
    eyes darted to one side and then the
    other... he licked his lips.... The three
    little pigs trotted around, scooped up
    straw, and trotted to the walls of their

house. Each time they brought the straw they had to reach higher and higher with both arms....

Cool-down

Use bells to make a light, tinkling sound and ask the children to move their fingers gently around their bodies, releasing any tension. Finally, they should take a deep breath and exhale slowly.

Structuring a dance session

It is important to explore the movement potential of language which the children enjoy in the classroom, such as rhymes, poems and stories, and the language used in other curriculum areas. Maths or science, for instance, can be reinforced in movement lessons; for example spatial and directional concepts such as behind and in front, or push and pull.

Structure these lessons so that you allow the children to have three to five minutes of warm-up, where you ask them to complete various stretching, bending and locomotor movements, using either percussion or language as stimuli. The movement part of the session can be inspired by any medium, but you should ensure that the movements you have selected to practise involve, wherever possible, the elements listed in the diagram above.

The actual dance part of the session should last about five to ten minutes and the children should be given ample opportunity to develop movement patterns performed on one spot, or creative sequences which travel, and to express themselves to a piece of music or a poem, putting all their movement training practices into simple dances.

Finally, the session should end with a quiet activity so that the children are prepared to make the transition back to the classroom.

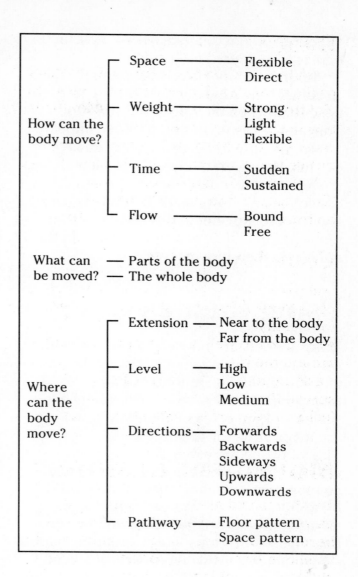

Whole body movement

To dance well a dancer's body must be in good condition. His muscles and joints must be strong and flexible to enable him to perform with balance and clarity of shape. Although no one should expect young children to dance perfectly, you should make sure that their dance lessons are not simply treated as a time for expressive and dramatic release.

Children at Key Stage 1 will already have made the quantum leap from using only their fingers and arms to express themselves, to being able to use their whole bodies. Even so, children often fail to use their trunks. Therefore, you should encourage them to make use of their hips, spines, shoulders and heads.

Children at Key Stage 1 also find it easier to control their movements from a static base than when moving about the room. They enjoy the invitation to move about freely and should be given every chance to do this. However, the quality of their movements may deteriorate as a consequence. However, if the children are given some movement directions as they move, there will be an improvement in the quality of their movements.

Using themes

Many schools are now using themes as the central core for much of the work they do with the children. Dance too, can be used to support theme work successfully and theme work itself can frequently provide the inspiration for creating a dance lesson. The following are examples of themes which can be used successfully in dance: communications; machines; mini-beasts; buildings; weather; seasons; my body; animals; prehistoric animals; sinking and floating; celebrations; magic; health; shape; environments; growing; water; fire; flight; circus.

As examples of how themes can be used, the themes of animals, communications, fire and growing have been expanded upon. The information is given in the form of ideas which can be extended and developed to suit your own needs and situations.

Theme: animals

The theme of animals is popular in primary schools, whether explored as a discrete package or as part of another project such as environments or festivals.

Start off your work on the theme of animals by working with the children in the classroom. Ask them to think of different categories of animals and write these on the board in the form of a diagram, as shown in the example which follows.

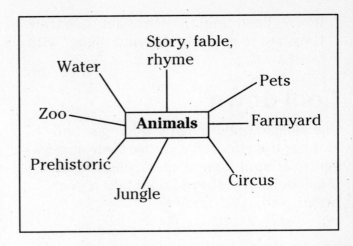

Having done this, ask the children to help you make a list of all the animals they can think of for each category. Talk about how these animals behave and move, and build up a movement profile on each one. You may end up with something like the following analyses on the elephant and monkey.

The elephant

• The elephant's movements are strong and purposeful.
• The elephant moves his trunk, legs and feet.
• He moves his trunk up and down and swings his legs and feet.

Using this analysis you could work on the following movement suggestions.
• Ask the children to pretend to be strong and heavy. As they move they should stamp their feet firmly on to the floor maintaining a steady rhythm.
• Encourage the children to lean forward from their hips as they move. They should swing one arm loosely from the shoulder to represent a trunk and can practise swinging their 'trunks' from side to side and upwards and downwards.
• Let the children practise curling their arms inwards towards their bodies to represent an elephant drinking. They should also try stretching their arms up high and curling them inwards to represent an elephant eating.
• Use a slow heavy drum beat or play 'The elephant' from *The Carnival of the Animals* by Saint-Saëns as the movement stimulus.

The monkey

• The monkey is quick, flexible, light and bouncy.
• She moves her face, fingers, arms, legs and tail.
• She moves forwards, backwards, sideways, upwards and downwards.

Using this analysis you could work on the following movement suggestions.
• Ask the children to pretend to be a monkey. They should walk flat-footed with their toes pointing away from their bodies and their knees bent and turned outwards. They can practise bouncing up and down on the spot from two feet to two feet.
• Tell the children to swing their arms loosely from their shoulders and move them from side to side.
• Ask the children to jump up and down keeping their knees bent and letting their arms flop from their shoulders.
• Tell the children to crouch down keeping their backs straight and letting their arms hang loosely. Can they move around the room in this position? Let them practise moving in all directions and show them how to use their arms to support them when moving faster.

• Ask the children to pretend to eat like a monkey. They should crouch down near to the floor, keeping a straight back, and reach up for food, peeling and eating it.

All these movements can be accompanied by the following stimuli:
• xylophones and chime bars;
• 'Dance of the tumblers' from *Snow Maiden* by Rimsky-Korsakov;
• extracts from *Animals on the Move* (series) (Level 8 extension readers) (1984, Ginn).

Theme: communications

As in the previous theme, begin by working with the children in the classroom and draw up a diagram showing the different methods we use to communicate.

Having completed this, ask the children to expand on some of the categories.

Home services

The children may think of some of the following in connection with home services: postmen and women, milk deliverers, refuse collectors, electricity and gas workers and so on.

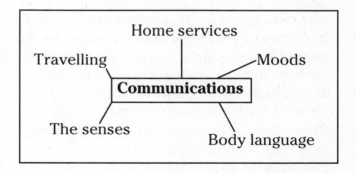

On this analysis movement could be stimulated by asking the children to pretend to be postmen and women carrying heavy sacks. They should walk slowly with bent knees, pressing each step firmly into the ground. They can then pretend to reach into their bags and post some letters, lifting the letter-box covers with one hand and posting the letters with the other.

Travelling

In this category the children may think of trains, buses, cars, aeroplanes, boats, bicycles and so on, and from these you could work on some of the following movement suggestions.
• The children can practise walking, running and skipping in different directions, forwards, backwards, circling to the right and to the left and stop.
• They can practise accelerating and decelerating when walking and running.
• Let the children practise obeying a stop signal. Use anything red to make the sign, for example, hold up a red bean bag.
• Arrange the children into pairs. One child in each pair should pretend to be a train and the other child should be a railway signal. When the arm of the signal is raised the train can proceed, but when it is down the train must stop.
• Ask the children to move up and down, pretending to be an aeroplane or a car travelling along a hilly road.

Body language

Body language is language without words. We all make gestures everyday to reinforce what we are saying or thinking or in response to what others say to us. A simple way of demonstrating body language to the children would be to test their reaction to some fairly outrageous suggestion such as, 'Before we start the lesson I am going to give you all ice-creams!'. Point out how their excitement is reinforced by jumping, laughing, waving and so on.

In relation to this work on some movement ideas. Ask the children to watch and copy you as you do the following:
• shake your finger angrily;
• cup a hand behind your ear;
• put your hand above your eyebrows to look at the far horizon;
• place both hands on your hips;
• raise your arm and clench your fist;
• raise your arm as if you were trying to gain attention in class;
• beckon with your hand.

The senses

Discuss hearing and listening with the children and work on some of the following movement suggestions:
• Ask the children to listen to various percussion instruments and respond by moving to the different sounds. For example, short, sharp, direct movements in response to castanets, sustained shaking and then a sudden, strong, whole body action in response to cymbals.
• Make a definite rhythmic beat on a drum and ask the children to respond by kicking their legs and punching with their arms. Then develop walking, running and jumping patterns using a variety of steps. Talk about how drums are used in some countries as a method of communication.
• Tap out S O S (••• – – – •••) on a chime bar ask the children to copy you by tapping on the floor, with their hands or feet.
• Ask the children to move around the room to music, first avoiding touching each other and then when they meet someone gently touching each others' hands.
• Arrange the children into pairs facing each other with their palms pressed together. They should then move their hands around the space between them, but keeping them joined. Can they move around the room when joined like this?

how fire moves, such as strong and light, spark, flame, short, curling, whirling, spiralling, fizz, crack, pop, twist, waver, quiver, flash, whizz, screech, explode, hot, burning, cascading, crackle, scatter.

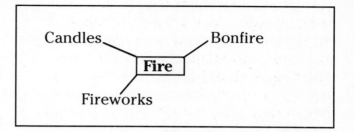

Fireworks

• Ask the children to pretend to be sparklers. They should move their fingers and hands making quick flicking movements, waving up and down.
• Ask the children to crouch down near to the floor and push their hands and arms upwards. They should move their arms and fingers high above their heads and down to their shoulders and back again in quick, angular movements.

NB: It is vital that children are warned of the dangers of playing with real fireworks.

Bonfire

Ask the children to listen to the 'Ritual fire dance' by De Falla. This should help the children when they are pretending to be a bonfire.

They should kneel down on the floor and tuck in their heads and hands. Tell them that the fire has just been lit and that they should bring out the fingers of one hand making a few short sharp movements. They should tuck them in again and do the same with their other hand and then both together. As the fire begins to get going, they should bring out their hands gently and smoothly to represent the smoke and larger flames. They can continue alternating the short, sharp movements with the smoother movements as they gradually stand up. The children can then crouch down again and begin to move their waists and hips in a circular motion, rising

Moods

Encourage the children to feel the different moods portrayed in various pieces of music. How do they feel, for example, when they hear *Danse Macabre* (Saint Saëns), 'Morning' from *Peer Gynt* (Grieg), 'Pastoral' *Symphony No. 6* (Beethoven), or disco music, or 'Mock Morris' by Percy Grainger, or 'Swing low sweet chariot', or 'Take five' by Paul Desmond and Iola Brubeck. Help the children to *feel* the music. Ask the children to suggest, various movements which will fit the music.

Theme: Fire

Work with the children before the dance lesson and draw up a diagram reflecting some different aspects of fire as in the example.

Help the children to build up a list of stimulating movement words to describe and falling until their waists, hips, shoulders and arms are all gyrating as fast as possible.

Candles

Ask the children to pretend to be tall, thin candles. They should wave their hands above their heads as if their hands were the flames. Gradually, they should bend their arms until their hands are on their heads and then gently and slowly pretend to melt until they are as small as possible. Can they make different candle shapes? Accompany these movements with sleigh bells.

Theme: growing

Work with the children before the dance session to build up a diagram showing some things that grow. You may end up with something resembling the diagram below.

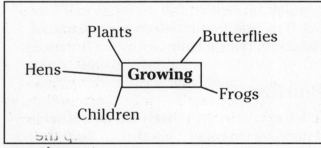

Plants

Again ask the children to expand this category by thinking of lots of different plants. Some examples of plants and movement suggestions are given below.
• Strawberry: the children should slowly and smoothly move along the ground and stop. They should then spread out their hands, arms and legs to represent the suckers.
• French bean: the children can make spiralling, smooth, flexible movements upwards and sideways.
• Cactus: the children can make short, sharp, quick movements, sticking their elbows and knees out at angles to make angular, spiky shapes.

Frogs

The children can act out the life cycle of a frog.
• Ask them to pretend to be frog-spawn. They should lie on the floor and sway from side to side and up and down. Encourage them to try to wobble like a mass of jelly.
• Tell them that they have now become tadpoles. They should lie on the floor and wiggle their legs and bodies keeping their arms by their sides.
• As the children pretend to grow into frogs they can begin to slide slowly along the ground, and then gradually begin to use their legs, until they rise up to a crouched position and leap around the room.

Butterflies

The children can act out the life cycle of a butterfly. Ask them to kneel down on the floor and bend forward until their chests and foreheads touch their knees. They should tuck in their arms along the sides of their bodies and keep very quiet and still as if they are a tiny butterfly egg on a leaf.

Talk to them about the caterpillar growing inside the egg and let the children start to move a little, shuffling on their lower legs and lifting their heads, moving more and more until the caterpillar emerges from the egg. Teach them the caterpillar movements from the gymnastics activities (see Chapter 1, page 18) and let them move about the area.

Ask the children to lie on the floor and gently roll over and over and from side to side until they lie still and stiff in a tucked, 'chrysalis' shape. Gradually, they should start to grow – first an antenna, until finally the wings break out of the chrysalis and gently stretch out to dry. The children can then delicately and quietly move about the room on tiptoe moving their arms up and down.

Hens

• Ask the children to curl up and lie still on the floor and pretend to be a chick in an egg. Gradually, they should start to grow, beginning to move their arms and legs and turn their heads from side to side.

• When they begin to break out of the egg the children should pretend to make short, sharp taps on the shell with their beaks. They should stretch their necks and clamber out of the shell and pretend to be taking their first wobbly steps as a newly hatched chick. They should shake their whole bodies to fluff up their feathers.

• Ask the children to pretend to get older. They should pretend to grow longer legs and start to strut around the room, lifting each knee high and reaching forward with each leg and placing their toes on the floor before their heels. They should jerk their heads from side to side like a hen, and tuck their arms into their bodies leaning forward from their hips to peck the ground.

Children

Ask the children to pretend to be newborn babies. They should lie on their backs and

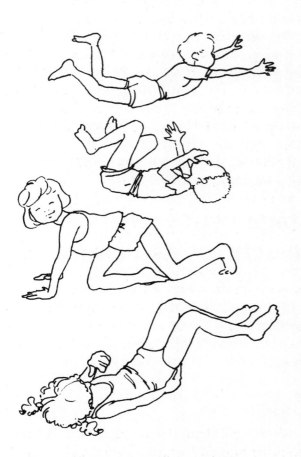

move their fingers and hands and turn their heads from side to side. They should then start to wave their arms, fingers and legs in the air. As they pretend to develop, the children should roll over on to their tummies and lift their heads. Gradually, they should start to crawl along the floor on their hands and knees.

Country dance

Country dancing can be introduced into the curriculum at any stage during Key Stage 1. However, if children are introduced to set dances too early, the essential essence of the dance – the aesthetic feeling which dancing freely to music generates – will be lost, for even though all children have some rhythm, not all have metric rhythm. Also, if you try to teach formal dancing too soon many children will not yet be confident enough in their surroundings to be able to dance. Therefore, it is a good idea to ensure that the children have worked through all the orientation lessons suggested earlier in this chapter and in Chapter 2 before they work on set dances. This foundation will allow the children to build and extend their natural rhythms, having become familiar with their bodies and the relationship between actions, songs and rhymes.

The children should build up to doing set pattern dances slowly. The 'play element' of this process should be maintained at all times and, initially, the children should be allowed to express themselves in an 'open-ended' way, moving gradually towards more structured situations. This way the children will begin to feel the quality of good, rhythmic movement patterns and begin to move more easily and gracefully in their general environment.

Introducing the children to rhythmic dancing will also involve them in gross motor and locomotor activity. This will help to refine their body control and to appreciate the ways in which their bodies can be used to good effect, developing both strength and stamina.

Music is obviously all important in rhythmic dance. Children have a natural response to modern music and can usually be observed tapping their feet and hands as they listen to it. Many children demonstrate similar responses when they sing songs. Open up the structure of dance lessons and allow them to feel the beat of the music. In this way, the children are not expected to conform to any structure which might restrict their movement freedom. To ask children in the early stages of their development to dance to strict counts of four or eight, to stop or start or turn on command is altogether too demanding. To do this is to turn expressive and enjoyable dancing into an inhibiting and boring activity.

The development of country dancing

The development of country dancing may be described as a four stage process:
• exploration;
• early structures and creativity;
• patterns and repetitions;
• rhythmic dances.

In each of the four stages the choice of musical accompaniment can determine the success or failure of the activity. If the children like the sound, then they will be motivated to move. For some children this motivation will come, for example, from the sound of a steel drum, and for others it may come from a well-known song. Children often seem to be more confident if they are asked to move to a familiar rhythm.

Stage one: exploration

At this stage it is much better if session structures are kept fairly free and informal. You can work on this material for two or three sessions and then change the songs, the movement poem, and the class march. Try the following progressive suggestions for activities.
• Play a piece of music and encourage the children to clap along. Let them stand up and sway from side to side to the music. The children can then walk and step, hop and skip to the music. Don't worry if they miss the beat! Try another piece of music.
• Play either of the two pieces of music and let the children move freely to it, but this time let them choose when to stop and when to move again.
• Try a 'word dance' where you say something like the following rhyme and the children do the actions:
    Clap hands together
    Shake them in the air
    Clap hands together
    Shake them in the air.
    Stamp, stamp, stamp
    Hop, hop, hop.
    Stamp hop stamp hop
    Let me stop.
• Use various poems and songs as stimuli for movement. Try, for example, 'Heads and shoulders, knees and toes', 'We all clap hands together', 'One finger, one thumb keep moving', 'Pat-a-cake, pat-a-cake', 'If you're happy and you know it, clap your hands', 'Run, rabbit, run', and 'Daddy wouldn't buy me a bow-wow'.
• Choose some marching music, for example, *The Stars and Stripes Forever* (Sousa) or the *Radetzky-Marsch* (Strauss) or better still 'The Grasshopper's Dance' (Bucalossi/Hylton). Ask the children to march freely to the music swinging their arms high and lifting their knees. You can end this session by leading the children as they march in a line back to the classroom!

Stage two: early structures and creativity

As soon as the children appear to be responding happily and rhythmically to the various musical stimuli in the first stage they will be ready to move on to this stage. Start the session by beating a drum, with your hand or a drumstick, so that it produces a clear distinguishable sound. Beat a steady rhythm and ask the children to run to the beat. If you are working with older children you can also introduce two quick beats which are repeated successively so that the children can skip. If you are not very confident about using percussion instruments in this way, you may find it helpful to move with the children as you beat the drum.

Change the pace of the beat to encourage the children to listen carefully and to alter their movements accordingly. Try beating a walking rhythm for eight counts, followed by eight running beats or skipping beats and then repeat this pattern.

Allow the children to choose the direction in which they travel and whether they walk forwards or backwards. When the drum beat changes, invite them to choose whether they run or skip forwards, backwards, or round in a circle.

Ask the children to sit down and to move one and then both arms to the beat of the drum. Ask them to clap their hands anywhere around their bodies to the beat of the drum. Then sit with the children in a circle and clap out a simple rhythm, for example four steady claps, and then ask the children to copy the rhythm. Add to the rhythm by, for example, clapping four steady claps and then tapping the floor with four steady beats. The children should join in until a steady rhythm is established. If you then stand up you can also incorporate foot stamping into the rhythm sequence.

Ask the children which parts of their body they can clap against. Ask them to try clapping against their right knees, the tops of their heads, the soles of their feet and so on. The children should then clap against these various different parts four times. Once they are confident and comfortable with the four beat rhythm let them create their own individual dances.

Ask the children to form a line and appoint one of them to act as leader. Practise walking in this formation to the beat of the drum. When the children are able to keep to this formation, stop beating the drum for a few seconds and ask them to choose two parts of their body to clap together four times. Beat the drum four times or count to four as they clap. This

lesson should be repeated at least once and then you can use the drum to create new rhythms such as eight beats and then an eight beat silence or four beats and then a four beat silence.

Stage three: patterns and repetitions

• Play the children some music with a steady beat and allow them to skip or walk to it, then suggest that the children clap their hands at the same time.
• Use the same music, but this time ask the children to stand in one place and clap their hands above their heads, behind their necks, high to their right and their left.
• Ask each child to choose a partner and let them play any clapping rhyme they know. Ask certain partnerships to demonstrate their clapping games to the rest of the class.

"My mother said that I never should

play with the goblins in the wood."

|| = clap own hands together
O = clap partner's hands

Encourage the children to extend their patterns by clapping other parts of their bodies such as knees, shoulders and heads.
• As a contrast to this static activity, ask the children to sing 'Half a pound of tuppeny rice' or a similar catchy, rhythmical song and let them skip freely around the room to the steady beat.

The children will now be ready to try a slightly more structured dance which may resemble the following example:
• ask them to face a partner and clap their right hands together four times and then clap their left hands together four times;

• ask them to clap both their hands with their partners' four times;

• ask them to clap their own hands four times;

• ask one child to stand still and clap his hands while his partner skips around him;

• ask the other child to stand still and clap while her partner skips round her.

While the children are practising these dances, play a song which the children all know, such as 'Pop goes the weasel' or a folk song, so that they can sing or hum as they clap.

Stage four: rhythmic dances

Having completed a number of sessions on each of the first three stages the children should be able to enjoy simple country dances.

A good way to introduce lessons which ultimately lead into simple formation dances would be as follows.

• Start with a general introduction, for example, 'I thought we would try this music today' (knowing it to be a favourite), and ask the children to skip, jump, clap and stamp freely to the music. Choose a few children who seem to be moving really well to the music to demonstrate so that the rest of the class understand and begin to see what you expect when you play rhythmical music.

• Move on to more specific movement training and ask all the children to stand still. Encourage them to bend and stretch, low, high and to either side of their bodies. Suggest that they use first one hand and then the other to lead the movement high to the right and the left, and low to the left and the right.

• Ask them to press their palms together and move them high to the right, high left, low right, low left and repeat.

• Ask the children what kind of step pattern they could make to the chosen music: should they walk, march or skip? Let them try out their own ideas and watch each other and choose. After choosing the basic step, suggest they make a pattern. Give them a few ideas if none are forthcoming, for example, 'Think about moving forwards and backwards on the same pathway. You might like to count to eight?' or, 'You might want to move around the space and then stop on the spot for a while.'

• Introduce more structure into the phrasing of the music so that the children know when to change direction. You should help by clapping the beats and thus leading the children. Help them to change from one type of movement to another by calling 'change' at the appropriate time. Phrasing is only recognised through practice. Let the children count as they move to help them pick up the beat.

• Ask the children to practise walking forwards for eight steps and backwards for eight steps and when most of the class are moving jauntily play the music for them to dance to.

• Introduce some country dance skills which the children can practise with a partner. Ask them to make right and then left-handed turns (eight beats); crossed hands, two-handed turns (eight beats); and, move forward to meet their partners and back again (16 beats).

Chapter 5
Outdoor and adventurous activities

'Pupils should:
- **explore the potential for physical activities within the immediate environment;**
- **undertake simple orientation activities;**
- **apply physical skills out of doors on suitable equipment;**
- **develop an awareness of basic safety practices'** (Programme of Study).

There are four ways through which these requirements can be met in Key Stage 1:
- using the school grounds;
- using nearby parks and playgrounds;
- combining physical education and geography;
- visiting other locations.

In this chapter, each of the areas listed above is discussed and suggestions are given which, it is hoped, will help teachers provide opportunities for outdoor and adventurous activities.

Using the school grounds

All schools ought to consider the potential of their grounds for providing children with outdoor and adventurous experiences. In doing so, the children are given the chance to be actively engaged in physical skill practices at least during play times and at lunch breaks. Many schools have already been able to create 'child friendly' environments in their immediate

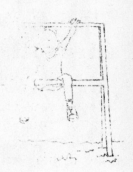

them, jump on and off
of them, balance on
one to another;
trees so that the children
find them and run around

frames embedded in the
plants grown along them, thus
arbour.
PVC or wooden blocks built
sting shape so that children
and jump down to and from
heights;
the play area, either built into a
one with proper steps;

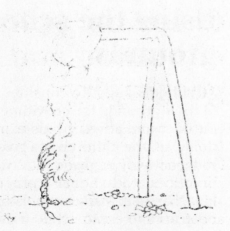

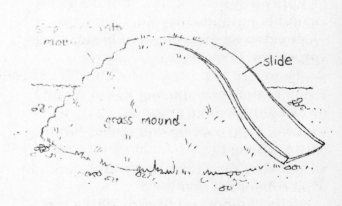

slide

grass mound.

• an old boat which the
in and out of and incorpor...
imaginative play;
• various playground m...
hopscotch grid, ...

Using near...
and playgr...

If it is impossible to ...
adventurous envir...
school grounds, the...
would be to take th...
park or playgro...
serve three p...
the child...
aware of ...
cross the ...
their teac...
children to
on the equi...
third, it woul...
opportunity to ...
rules governing s...
playgrounds ge...
that even where chi...
a school environment ...
their activities, a visit to ...
worth undertaking if on...
reasons mentioned abo...

Once in the playgro...
explain to the children how to use the
equipment safely and how they shoul...
behave both on and around the equipment.
For example:
• don't climb high until you've practised at
a lower height;
• make sure that when you climb up,
you've enough energy to come down safely;
• don't run in front of any moving
equipment;
• wait until the equipment has stopped
before you step off, stand, or sit on it;
• always hold moving equipment firmly
with both hands;
• keep your eyes open and watch carefully
what others are doing.

It is still important to provide a short
warm-up for the children before they move

...encourage ... ...
... ...ey had to cr...
... ...ing about ...
... ...bout ...
on various textures ...

Combining physical
education and
geography

One of the recommendations in Geography
in the National Curriculum (199?) ... the
Programme of Study for Key Sta... is to
allow children to acquire geogra... al
skills 'based on direct experien... practical
activities and explo...tion of the ...
As a result, many teachers are already

beginning to introduce children to simple orientation and navigation practices concerned with mapping and fieldwork techniques. The connections and parallels with similar goals in physical education make the two subjects obvious candidates for some form of integrated approach to teaching. In practical terms, those children who will eventually want to enjoy fell walking and orienteering will undoubtedly benefit and have their pleasure enhanced by understanding the simple skills of, say, navigation. Navigation by using a map is certainly within the scope of children in Key Stage 1. Admittedly, it may be more realistic, at this stage, to define navigation as a means of finding one's way about the school playground or the immediate neighbourhood, but the principle is the same. A lot of emphasis can be placed on simple plans, maps or routes and the nature of symbolic representation can be explored.

Visits to other locations

Most children in Key Stage 1 are taken on trips to locations which are not in their immediate environment, perhaps as part of a central topic which is being studied in the classroom. For some, this may be an annual visit which is organised as a special outing, while for others it could be one of several visits aimed to coincide with carefully planned topics throughout the year. Often, class teachers choose a location which adds another dimension to the topic being studied, for example, the seashore, a theme park, or a museum. Frequently, these visits last for a whole day to ensure that the children have 'real' experiences of several areas of the subjects being studied. In providing a broad, well-balanced day, all teachers ought to consider letting their children have some exercise. Many sites, for example, may be geared up to cater for young children's needs in this respect. There could be suitable equipment for

children to practise on and develop their skills out of doors. There may be opportunities for children to run up and down grassy banks, to run around trees and bushes, to climb on climbing frames or to use slides, swings and see-saws.

If the location is the seaside then a different set of activities would be available such as paddling, running on the sand, tackling sand-dunes and so on. Many games which are played in school can now be transferred to the beach and will take on a whole new dimension when set in different surroundings.

Some part of the day, therefore, should be set aside when you and the children can explore together the outdoor and adventurous physical activities afforded by half day or whole day visits to different locations.

Key Stage 2

Chapter 6
Gymnastic activities

'...Gymnastic activities focus on the body. They are concerned with acquiring control, co-ordination and versatility in the use of the body in increasingly challenging situations and with developing strength, especially of the upper body, and maintaining flexibility. These activities are based on natural actions such as leaping, balancing, inverting, rolling and swinging' (*PE for ages 5 to 16*, 1991).

The programme of study for gymnastic activities states that:
'Pupils should:
• **be enabled, both on the floor and using apparatus, to find more ways of rolling, jumping, swinging, balancing and taking weight on hands, and to adapt, practise and refine these actions;**
• **be guided to perform in a controlled manner and to understand that the ending of one action can become the beginning of the next;**

• **be given opportunities both on the floor and using apparatus in response to set tasks, to explore, select, develop, practise and refine a londer series of actions making increasingly complex movement sequences which they are able to repeat;**
• **be enabled to respond to a variety of tasks, alone or with a partner, emphasising changing shape, speed and direction through gymnastic actions.'**

In gymnastics, we are primarily concerned with the gross motor development of children; through which they learn both to manage and to exercise their bodies. A progressive programme of gymnastics, therefore, should enable children to develop the physical qualities which will help them to meet the challenges of the environment in which they live.

Gymnastics, however, should be concerned with more than just the capacity to develop children's physical potential. In addition, it should be concerned with the acquisition of skills, aesthetics, creativity and cognition. In order to achieve this, all teachers should be prepared to be flexible in the way in which they approach their teaching programmes. This is especially true when considering the suitability of a particular method or style of teaching. For example, skill based learning is often better acquired through adopting a direct approach, which would be totally inappropriate when looking at the creation and aesthetic appreciation of movement sequences.

This chapter provides a series of lessons which are appropriate for Key Stage 2, centred around four fundamental activities:
• locomotion;
• balance;
• rotation;
• flight.

These activities will form the basis of all the lessons and from them many different actions and sequences will be developed. Within the framework of each lesson, the children will be asked to respond to particular movement tasks either on the floor or on apparatus.

In order that bodily skills and concepts can be developed progressively each of the four fundamental activities will be 'revisited' at various times throughout Key Stage 2. There will be, of course, an essential overlapping of the fundamental activities in order to produce more creative, aesthetic and skilful movements.

A useful way to see the overall impact of this work would be to present the work in units, one for each term. Each unit would consist of between ten and twelve lessons, each constructed in the following way:
• three to five minutes of warm-up;
• five to ten minutes of skill training;
• fifteen minutes working on intermediary or large apparatus;
• three to five minutes of strength activity;
• two minutes of cool-down.

Initially in their lessons, the children should be encouraged to maintain the flexibility of their bodies by exercising their muscles to their limit and to develop body strength, particularly upper body strength. In everyday activities children seldom move their muscles and joints through the full range of possible movements. It is only when they need to attempt an action beyond the normal routine that they may realise their own lack of mobility. During gymnastic lessons the children should get into the habit of stretching their muscles fully. They should make a conscious effort to stretch them slowly, to a point where they start to hurt a *little*, as this will ensure they are using their bodies' full range of movements. The emphasis must be on stretching *slowly* to avoid injury.

Strength can only be increased by working the muscles into an 'overload situation'. This means either making the muscles work harder or more often. The warm-up part of each session should, therefore, contain some flexibility exercises, in addition to the strength building part of the session.

It is important to ensure that the children produce good quality movements. They should be expected to think about the shape of their bodies as they move and they should be encouraged to use various degrees of muscle control to maintain 'good posture' throughout their movement actions and sequences. They should also be expected to vary the speed and direction of their movements and to consider the most effective level at which to work.

Warm-up

Every session should begin with a period of warm-up in which children stretch their muscles and increase their breathing rates. The following activities can be used to start any gymnastic session in Key Stage 2. Select two or three from the following list for each session and work on them until the children are 'huffing and puffing!'
• Ask the children to jog anywhere, changing direction at will.
• Ask the children to jog and then touch

the floor when they hear the command.
• Ask them to jog, then sprint, jog and then sprint.
• Ask them to run and jump high in the air.
• Ask the children to make side-slipping steps with their right legs leading. They should step to the right, with their right feet, and then 'slip' their left feet across the floor to join their right feet, transferring their weight to their left feet in order to start again from the right. Ask them to do the same but with their left legs leading.
• Ask the children to jog around the room and then, on hearing the command, to jump on the spot.
• Ask the children to run, skip and jump around the room.
• Ask them to leap from one of their feet to the other.
• Ask them to walk on tiptoe and then on their heels. How quickly can they do this?
• Ask the children to run and then stop suddenly. They should repeat this a number of times.
• Ask the children to jog around the room and then, on hearing the appropriate command, they should curl up or stretch up high.
• Ask the children to stand up, lie down, kneel down, stand up, curl up and so on.
• Ask them to jog around the room and sit down when they hear the command. They

should repeat this a number of times.
• Ask them to jog forwards, backwards and sideways.
• Ask the children to run and jump, turning in the air.
• Ask them to run anywhere in the room and on hearing the calls, 'stomach', 'bottom' or 'knees' they should place that particular part of their bodies on to the floor.
• Ask the children to 'walk' around the room on their bottoms and feet only. Can they move forwards and backwards?
• Ask the children to walk crouched down near to the ground, and then stretched up as tall as possible away from the ground.
• Ask the children to stretch up high and then to curl down low.
• Ask them to run and jump and make a stretched shape in the air.
• Ask them to move around the room with their feet as far away from their hands as possible.
• Ask the children to jump about the room, first making low level jumps and then stretched, high jumps, with their feet and ankles pressed together.
• Ask them to run and jump into the air. They should sink to the ground, stretch out and then roll sideways. They should repeat this several times.
• Ask the children to jog around the room. When they hear the command to stop they should make a stretched high or curled low shape on the floor.
• Ask the children to curl up and jump around the room on two feet.
• Ask them to jump from two feet to one foot and then back on to two feet again.
• Ask the children to jump on the spot. They should start off by making fairly low jumps and gradually jump higher and higher. They can then jump around the room on two feet.
• Ask the children to move around the room making three stretched leaps, three jumps and three hops.
• Ask them to take bounding strides and then change to short steps on the spot and back to long strides again.
• Ask the children to stand on the spot and

in turn, lift their knees up high. They should gradually increase the speed.
• Ask them to run and then touch the floor with their left hands. They should run again and touch the floor with their right hands. Finally, they should run and touch the floor with both hands.
• Ask the children to sit in the straddle position and touch their toes. Can they put their stomachs on the floor? Ask them to see how far they can get.
• Ask them to make wide circling actions at the sides of their bodies with each of their arms in turn.
• Ask the children to lift both shoulders up towards their ears and back down again.
• Ask them to lie down and lift one of their knees and then the other on to their chests and put them down again, one at a time.
• Ask the children to hold the top of their left feet with their right hands, behind their backs, and gently pull their left heels on to their bottoms.

Partner work

• Arrange the children into pairs and ask one child in each pair to lead his partner around the room running, jumping and skipping as they go.
• Arrange the children into pairs, face to face. One child in each pair should make various movements and the other child should copy her. They should make their movements as big as they can.
• With the children in pairs, one child in each pair should curl up small and the other child should jump over him, land and then curl up. The first child should then jump over the second and so on.
• Ask the children to choose a partner. The pairs should run around the room one behind the other and then swap over so that the other child in each pair is the leader. Repeat this several times.
• Ask the children to hold hands with a partner. They should face each other and slip-step sideways.
• Ask the children to choose partners. They should then hop together, jump together and skip together, side by side.

Strength activities

Choose one or two strength activities for each lesson. It is essential that the children work the part of the body which has been selected for strengthening until they begin to hurt a *little*.

Leg strengthening

• Ask the children to hop on one of their feet and then the other.
• Ask them to hop from side to side, one foot to the other.
• Ask the children to jump on one of their feet and lift the knee of their other leg high. They should alternate the action.
• Ask the children to stand on tiptoe and then rock back so that they are standing on their heels.
• Ask them to jump from two feet and land on two feet.
• Ask the children to stand with their legs shoulder width apart. They should keep their backs straight and bend and straighten their knees.
• Ask the children to keep their backs straight and lunge forward with each foot as far as possible.
• Ask them to stand up and then kneel down, and stand up and so on. They must keep their backs straight the whole time. Can they do this with their arms folded?
• Ask the children to swing one leg high in the air and then the other, keeping them straight.

Arm strengthening

• Ask the children to stand about one long stride from a wall. Tell them to lean forward with their arms outstretched so that they fall on to the wall and then push their bodies away from the wall so that they are once again standing up straight.
• Ask the children to shake hands with a partner and then, still holding hands, pull away against each other.
• Ask the children to stand up and stretch one of their arms and then the other as high as possible.

• Ask the children to move like a caterpillar. They should crouch down and put their weight on their feet. They should transfer their body weight to their hands and then walk their hands forward until their bodies are stretched out. They should then keep their hands still and walk their feet up to their hands, until they return to the initial crouched position.

• Ask the children to put their weight on their hands and feet with their backs facing the floor. They can then move forwards, backwards and sideways.

They should lift their right legs in the air, then lift their left legs in the air and also try jumping from one foot to the other.

• Ask the children to put their weight on their hands and feet, and face the floor. They should reach out with their hands until their arms, spines and legs are fully stretched. Ask them to hold the position for as long as they can.

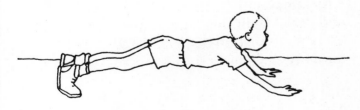

Keeping the same position and their feet in the same place, ask the children to walk their hands around their bodies until they have completed a full circle.

They could also try lifting their hands off the floor, one at a time, and stretching their arms.

Can they take both their hands off the floor and clap?

• Ask the children to try 'walking' like a seal. This time they should take their weight off their feet and move their bodies forward on their hands and arms and drag their legs along the floor.

• Finally, they could rotate their bodies until their backs are facing the floor.

Spine and hip strengthening

• Ask the children to kneel with their arms folded and then sit on the floor to the right of their bodies and then kneel again. They should repeat this process but sitting to the left of their bodies this time. This activity will also help to increase flexibility.

• Ask the children to sit down with their legs in the straddle position. Ask them to keep their backs straight and stroke the inside of one of their legs with the sole of their other foot. This activity will also help to increase flexibility.

• Ask the children to lie down and, keeping their spines and legs straight, each lift one of their legs slowly into the air, and slowly put them down again and then repeat with their other legs.

• Ask the children to kneel down and put one of their hands on the floor. They should each thread their other arm between the supporting arm and the knee on the same side and twist their spines so that their hands can reach as far as possible. This activity will also help to increase flexibility.

• Ask the children to kneel down and put both of their hands flat on the floor. They should then arch their spines. This activity will also help increase flexibility.

• Ask the children to kneel down and place their hands on the floor. Ask them to each lift one knee underneath their bodies and touch their foreheads and then stretch that leg as far as possible behind their bodies.

• Ask the children to stand with their feet about shoulder width apart and then circle their hips. This activity will also help to increase flexibility.

• Ask the children to kneel down and walk their hands on the floor around their bodies, they must keep their knees and feet still while they do this. This activity will also help to increase flexibility.

• Ask the children to lie on their backs and lift both their legs off the ground. They should keep their legs straight and then part them, moving their legs up and down and from side to side.

• Ask the children to lie on their stomachs and hold their hands behind their backs and lift their chests off the floor. Ask them to do this again, but this time lifting both their chests and legs off the floor.

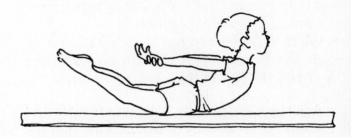

• Ask the children to lie on their backs with their knees bent and lift and roll their trunks until their bottoms are off the floor. This activity will also help to increase flexibility.

• Ask the children to lie on their stomachs and grasp their ankles with their hands. They should try to straighten their legs as far as they can.

90

• Arrange the children into pairs and ask each child to face her partner and hold each other's wrists. They should then make a sawing action with their arms.
• Ask the children to sit in a straddle position and try to put their stomachs on to the floor. This activity will also increase flexibility.
• Ask the children to do some bent-knee sit-ups.

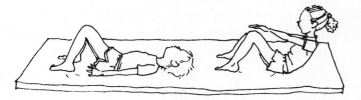

Cool-down

• Ask the children to stand up straight and check their posture by imagining a plumb-line running down from the back of their necks through their hips, knees and ankles. Once you have established good posture, ask the children to walk while maintaining it. They should keep their heads erect with their eyes looking forward and their stomachs and bottoms pulled in.
• Ask the children to lie down on the floor and tense and relax their bodies.
• Tell the children to lie down and roll over on their stomachs. They must keep their arms and legs off the ground as they roll.

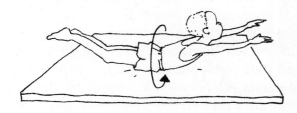

• Tell the children to sit in the straddle position with their legs stretched out in front of them. They should then change their position so that they are sitting cross-legged with straight backs.
• Ask the children to lie on their stomachs.

They should then try to use their hands and arms to lift their bodies up and down.
• Tell the children to lie on their backs, lift their legs and kick them up and down in a scissor action.
• Ask the children to choose partners. One child in each partnership should make different walking pathways around the room while the other child follows.
• Ask the children to stretch their arms up high and then out wide and finally place them at the sides of their bodies.
• Touch different parts of your body and ask the children to touch their bodies in the same way without making a sound.
• Make various different positions with your arms and ask the children to copy you, again without making a sound.
• Form the children into a large circle and walk around the room.
• Ask the children to make symmetrical shapes with their arms.
• Ask the children to bend and stretch their arms at different levels around their bodies.
• Ask the children to shake their hands and feet.
• Tell the children to bend down low and stretch up high. Ask them to lie down and curl up and then stretch out and stand up.
• Ask the children to walk round in a small circle, first clockwise and then anticlockwise.
• How long can each child stand on one leg?

At the end of the cool-down session ask the children to stand still again, making sure that their posture is good, and where possible, tell them to walk quietly back to the classroom.

Units of work

The rest of this chapter is concerned with skill learning and apparatus work, which should make up the major part of a gymnastic lesson. The units of work are grouped into four sections according to the different age groups they cover. Each unit of work is designed to explore a principal theme and is sub-divided into various themes. The material should be worked on in the order it is presented, as the activities become progressively more demanding.

However, activities can be repeated and indeed, if the children are to present good quality work, repetition will be essential.

As you observe and instruct the children ask yourself the following questions.
• Are the children maintaining good body tension. For example, are their legs and feet stretched as far as possible? Are their spines straight? Are their body shapes clear?
• Do sequences flow? Are there smooth changes from one body position or method of travel to another?
• Do the children use a variety of different movements in their sequences?
• Is it possible for the children to be active at other levels, such as near to the ground or high in the air?
• Are the 'gifted' children being challenged? Is the task provided suitable for the less able children? Do you need to provide a different task for any disabled children?

It is important from time to time to select children to demonstrate their work to the rest of the class. Children will find it easier to perfect their movements as they watch their peers and demonstrations could illustrate:
• a good starting position;
• clear body shapes;
• a variety of movements;
• good use of floor space and apparatus;
• movements showing a variety of speeds;
• good, smooth transitions from movement to movement;
• a good finishing position.

Eventually, after the children have begun to perfect their sequences, one or two children should be chosen to show their sequences to the rest of the class. Follow-up by holding a general discussion about the sequences.

Units of work for Year 3

Each unit in this section will provide a term's work.

Unit one: travelling 1

Travelling on feet

Skill training

• Ask the children to jog, skip, run, hop, leap, jump and walk at different speeds, levels and in different directions.
• Tell the children to jump around the room. Encourage them to practise the five basic jumps; jumping from two feet to two feet, two feet to one foot, one foot to the other foot, one foot to two feet and one foot to the same foot. Also ask them to jump with their feet together and apart.

Intermediary apparatus

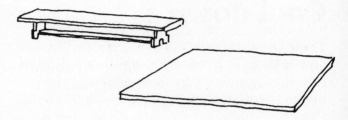

• Ask the children to use the bench, mat and floor to practise all the methods of travelling which they used in the floorwork.
• Let the children choose three different ways of travelling on their feet and ask them to use each method to travel along the bench, mat and floor.
• Help the children to construct movement sequences. They should choose a good starting position, select three or four different methods of travelling on their feet and end the sequence standing straight, with their heads erect, their eyes looking forwards, their bottoms pulled in, their shoulders down, feet together and their hands at their sides.

Travelling on hands and feet: 1

Skill training

• Ask the children to travel on the ground, on their hands and feet. Tell them to move

backwards, sideways and in circles.
• Ask the children to travel on their hands and feet, but this time so that their stomachs are facing the ceiling. Can they move sideways like a crab?
• Teach the children to do 'bunny jumps'. They should put their hands flat on to the floor and press down on to the ground. Tell them to make sure that they keep their arms straight, locking the elbow joints. Then, keeping their heads forward to prevent the body toppling over, they should kick both legs in the air making sure that their feet and ankles stay pressed together. The children can then travel around the room using bunny jumps.
• Show the children how to bunny jump with a twist. They should put their weight on to their hands, kick their legs in the air and put their feet down at the side of their hands.
• Ask the children to make 'cat-springs'. They should push off from both their feet and spring on to both their hands, quickly bringing their feet up to their hands to support their body weight.

Intermediary apparatus

Ask the children to set out mats so that they have a mat each.
• Ask them to travel across their mats on their hands and feet in any way they choose. Then ask them to cross their mats on their hands and feet but with their stomachs facing the ceiling and then their backs facing the ceiling.
• Ask the children to make up a sequence. They should first travel on the floor in front of the mat, then travel across the mat, and finally return to their starting place. The only way they are allowed to travel is on their hands and feet and they should use three different methods.

Travelling on hands and feet: 2

Skill training

The children should be given the opportunity to repeat the skill training session from the previous sub-theme. They should be encouraged to move continuously and show a variety of methods of travelling.

Large apparatus

Set out the apparatus as shown below and ask the children to find ways of travelling on it using their hands and feet together.

Encourage the children to find different starting places on the apparatus to begin their travelling; and when leaving the apparatus they should try and leave from their hands. They should grip the apparatus with their hands, keeping their arms firm, and push away to land on their feet.

On some pieces of apparatus the children may be able to land on their hands alone. Can they find out which? Can they go over the apparatus on their hands alone and land on their feet?

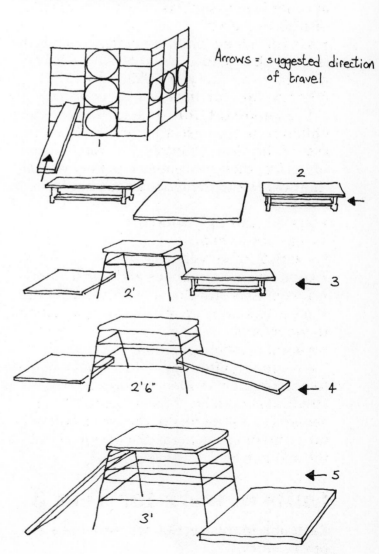

Arrows = suggested direction of travel

Large apparatus

Set the apparatus out as shown below and let the children practise some of the following movement tasks.

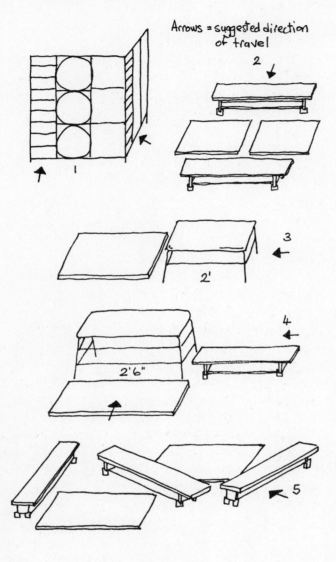

Arrows = suggested direction of travel

• Let the children explore the apparatus so that they find the places where they can balance on different parts of their bodies. Children who are working at the climbing frame should be encouraged to try and hang upside down from their knees from the bars and from their hands on the ropes. Some children may even be able to get on to the frame from a shoulder standing balance on the floor, putting their legs over the bar and pulling themselves up on to the frame.
• Let the children choose three or four balances and make clear body shapes.

They should find linking the movements which will allow them to make a complete sequence on the apparatus.

Unit three: travelling 2

Travelling on different body parts: 1

Skill training

• Let the children demonstrate their knowledge about the different ways in which they can use their feet to travel and their ability to travel in different ways on their hands and feet.
   Remind the children that they should move in different directions and create good body positions.
• Ask the children to lie on their backs and try and propel themselves across the floor with their feet.
• Ask the children to lie down on their stomachs and try and propel themselves with their hands and feet.
• Tell the children to roll across the floor sideways by moving from their stomachs to their sides and on to their backs.
• Ask the children to try and pull themselves across the room on their hands and knees, moving their arms forward and sliding their legs along the ground.
• Ask the children to move about the room on two parts of their bodies, for example bottoms and hands, knees and hands and so on.

Travelling on different body parts: 2

Skill training

• Ask the children to practise travelling on two parts of their bodies at the same time.
• Tell the children to practise travelling on three parts of their bodies at the same time.
• Ask them to lie on the floor and stretch out, with their arms above their heads, and then roll across the floor keeping their arms and legs stretched.
• Ask the children to curl up on their sides and then roll over the floor staying in the same shape.

96

Intermediary apparatus

Let the children fetch and set out their mats in a space, ensuring that each child has his own mat.

• Revise the correct technique for doing a forward roll (see page 28) and allow the children to practise them on their mats.

• Revise with the children the correct way to do a backward roll (see page 28) and let the children practise these on their mats.

• Allow the children to choose which rolls they would like to practise.

Travelling on different body parts: 3

Skill training

• Ask the children to kneel down and pull and push themselves along. Can they lie on their stomachs and backs and do the same?

• Tell the children to try rolling, pushing, pulling, rocking and spinning to move themselves about on the floor.

Large apparatus

Let the children help you to set out the apparatus as shown on this page and then work on the following movement tasks.

• Ask the children to travel on the apparatus and the floor around it, using different parts of their bodies.

• Can they make up sequences on and around the apparatus in which they include rolling, pushing, pulling and jumping movements?

Units of work for Year 4

There are three units of work for Year 4, the first unit has five sub-themes, the second has three sub-themes and the third has four sub-themes.

Unit one: travelling

Jumping and landing: 1

Skill training

• Ask the children to jump on the spot. Emphasise that they should stretch their

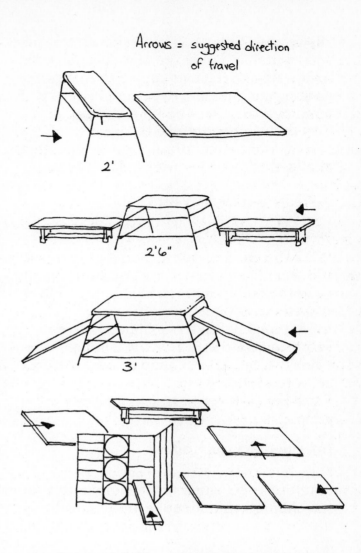

Arrows = suggested direction of travel

2'

2'6"

3'

toes, feet and ankles as well as their knees and legs.

• Ask them then to jump high on the spot and make a quarter turn in the air before landing.

• Tell the children to run, jump from one foot and land on the other.

• Tell them to run, jump in the air, make a quarter turn before landing and continue running. They should repeat this several times.

• Ask the children to each find a partner. One child in each pair should kneel down close to the floor. The other child can then jump over her partner, then run and jump over everyone else's partner. The children can then change places.

Intermediary apparatus

With the children, set out the mats for them to try these movement tasks. Ask the children to run and jump high into the air and land on the mat. Then ask them to run and try to jump over the mat. Ask one child to curl up and tell everyone else to practise running and jumping over him. Can they jump over another child but with a half turn in the air? Continue to stress throughout the importance of bending their ankles and knees in order to land safely.

Jumping and landing: 2

Skill training

• Ask the children to run and jump around the area. They can choose any sort of jump.
• Let the children practise jumping from two feet to two feet.
• Tell the children to run, jump in the air and change direction for the landing.
• Ask the children to jump around the area on both of their feet.
• Ask the children to run, jump, land and jump again.

Intermediary apparatus

Shown below is the safest (and most uninteresting) set up for the apparatus. All the children should move in the same direction and return in the same direction.

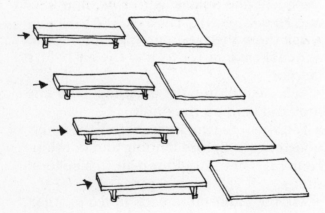

However, you can also set up more interesting and less 'military' looking apparatus.
   Let the children help you to set out the benches and mats and then practise the following movement tasks.
• Ask the children to walk along the bench and jump off the end on to the mat.

• Ask the children to run along the bench and jump off the end on to the mat.
• Ask the children to jump along the bench, keeping both their feet together.
• Ask the children to step on to the bench from the side, and then push themselves high into the air, landing with both feet on the bench.

Jumping and landing: 3

Skill training

Let the children choose which running, jumping and landing exercises they wish to practise.

Large apparatus

Set out, with the children's help, the apparatus into five sections.

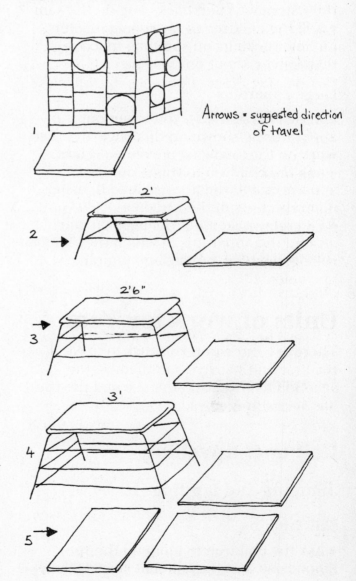

Arrows = suggested direction of travel

Arrange the children into five groups and ask the children working on the first four sets of apparatus to get on to their apparatus and jump off again. The children working on the fifth set of apparatus should try and jump over the first mat and land on the second mat.

Jumping and rolling: 1

Skill training

• Ask the children to stretch out on to the floor and practise rolling sideways. They should also try curling up on the floor and rolling sideways.
• Tell the children to jump on the spot.
• Ask the children to sit in the straddle position and then rock from side to side.

Intermediary apparatus

Let the children set out mats in a space. Ensure that each child has their own mat.
• Ask the children to practise rolling across the mat. Let them choose which rolls they practise.
• Ask the children to practise rolling backwards. They should finish so that their feet are wide apart. Can they finish in the same position when rolling forwards?
• Ask the children to run towards their mats and jump high in the air. They should land and roll on the mat.

Jumping and rolling: 2

Skill training

Let the children have a period of free practice in which they can practise running, jumping and landing.

Large apparatus

Set up the apparatus as shown on page 98. The children can then try working on the following movement tasks.
• Ask the children to get on to the apparatus and then jump off on to the mat. They should do the same again, but this time turn in the air so that they land facing the apparatus.
• Ask the children to climb on to the apparatus and jump off it again, rolling over

as they land on the mat. They can practise different rolls as they land; for example, they can roll backwards with their feet together or apart, they can roll sideways when curled up or stretched out, and they can roll forwards with their feet together or apart.

Unit two: balance

Balancing on hands and heads

Skill training

• Help the children to revise the work they did on balancing on large and small parts of the bodies (see pages 24–26).
• Help them to do a handstand. They will need to have strong arms and shoulders, and an ability to hold their bodies in tension if they are to do this skill effectively.

Ask the children to lie down and stretch their arms above their heads tensing their whole bodies. Explain to them that this is the amount of tension they will need if they are to perform a handstand properly.

They should then crouch down and put their hands flat on to the floor about a shoulder width apart with their fingers pointing forwards. They should look just in front of their hands.

Tell the children to straighten their legs and swing one straight leg into the air, keeping the other leg safely grounded. Let them practise this before progressing any further, and indeed a full handstand should not be attempted at this stage without teacher support.

Intermediary apparatus

Ask the children to set out mats. For the first activity they should be placed about 15cm from a wall.
• Ask the children to make a headstand (see page 25). By working on a mat placed near to a wall the children should not over-balance.

• Ask the children to practise a shoulder balance. They can practise initially, balancing with their legs and feet pressed together and stretched straight in the air and then move their legs into different positions.

Balance into rolling

Skill training

• Let the children practise doing a handstand, but they should still keep one leg on the ground.
• Ask them to practise a shoulder balance.
• Let them also try balancing on one hip or one knee or one foot.
• Ask the children to practise a shoulder balance. They should then over-balance into a roll.
• Ask the children to practise balancing on other parts of their bodies, and over-balancing into rolls.

Intermediary apparatus

Let the children set out the mats. Ask them to practise a headstand. You should assist any children who need help. Ask the children to balance on one part of their bodies and then tip into a roll. While the children work on this, you should work with them in turn to support their full handstands. You should always remind the children that they must press down on to flat hands and keep their arms straight. Make sure that you keep your head by the children's hips so that you aren't kicked as they swing their legs up. You should catch the children where their pelvises join their legs.

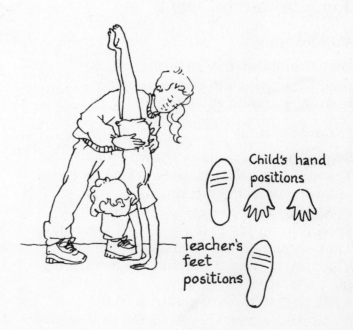

Child's hand positions

Teacher's feet positions

Balance and travelling: 1

Skill training

Ask the children to balance on a large body part, stretching as much as possible, and either tip into a roll or tip on to their feet and travel across the floor. For example, they may choose to balance on the lower part of one of their legs, tip sideways into a curled, sideways roll and then stand up and bound around the room.

Intermediary apparatus

Let the children help you to set out benches and mats.
• Ask the children to run along a bench and jump off the end, rolling and holding a balance on the mat.
• Ask the children to run up to the bench, jump on to it and then jump across it, jumping off the end, rolling and holding a balance on the mat.
• Tell the children to reverse the movement sequence so that they start off balancing on the mat and then tipping into a roll, jumping on to and across the bench, finishing back in their original starting place.

Balance and travelling: 2

Skill training

Let the children choose and practise a selection of balancing and travelling activities.

Intermediary apparatus

Let the children help you to set out some mats so that they are placed in pairs end to end. The children can then do a headstand, curl up and roll over and over. They should repeat this using a shoulder balance.

Ask the children to travel over and across a bench by making bunny jumps (see page 100). Encourage them to raise their hips higher and higher and hold the position for as long as possible.

Large apparatus

Ask the children to help you set out a movement table and mat. The children can then work on the following tasks.
• Tell them to run up to the table and bunny jump on to it. They should lie on their stomachs and reach down on to the mat, forming a handstand. They should slowly curl up and roll over forwards.

• Ask the children to run up to and jump on to the table, landing on their hands and the lower part of one of their legs. They should hold this balance on the apparatus and then choose another balance to move into and hold. Finally, they should stand up, jump off the table and land and roll.

101

• Ask the children to practise balancing against a climbing frame. When they come out of the balance they should curl up and roll over and over.
• Ask the children to climb on to the climbing frame and hang down from their knees, reaching down on to the mat with their hands. Slowly, they should kick their legs over and curl up and roll.

Unit three: flight

When looking at flight let the children use the apparatus which they have been working on in previous weeks, but also add a sloping bench to the climbing frame. Give the children the opportunity to work on each piece of apparatus, working on flight patterns both on to and off the apparatus. They should be encouraged to work up to the correct speed for take-off, keep the right tension to hold a good body shape in the air, and have a sufficiently controlled release of tension to land safely and stop the forward motion of the movement.

Methods of take-off

Skill training

Ask the children to practise all the different ways of taking off and landing:
• take off from two feet and land on two feet together;
• take off from two feet apart to land on two feet apart;
• run and take off from one foot and land on two feet together;
• run and take off from one foot and land with both feet apart;
• run, take off from one foot and make a scissor action in the air;
• run, take off from one foot and complete a half turn in the air.

Intermediary apparatus

Ask the children to help you set out benches and mats. They can then work in groups on the apparatus and you should change the groups to different apparatus once each child has completed several turns.

• Ask them to practise running along a bench, taking off from one foot and getting as high into the air as possible.
• Ask the children to run towards the mat, take-off and jump as far as possible.

Flight and shape

Skill training

• Let the children revise the different types of take-offs (see above).
• Ask them to run and jump as high as they can, then run and jump as far as possible.
• Tell the children to run and make a star shape, a stretched shape and a tucked shape in the air.

Encourage the children to experiment using different take-offs when working on these activities and similarly ask them to consider appropriate landings.

Intermediary apparatus

Let the children help you to set out benches and mats. Ask them to practise running along the benches and jumping off the end making stretched, tucked and star shapes, landing on a mat. How many other shapes can they make in the air?

Flight and action

Skill training

• Ask the children to run, jump and turn in the air.
• Ask the children to run, jump and make a twisted shape in the air.
• Ask the children to run, jump and move their legs and then their arms in the air.
• Ask them to run, jump, and land on both feet with their ankles, knees and hips bent. This activity will also help flexibility.
• Ask the children to run and jump, landing on one foot before the other, keeping their centres of gravity of their bodies low and bending their knees.

Intermediary apparatus

Set out benches and mats and ask the children to repeat the running and jumping activities, making shapes and moving their arms and legs as they land on the mats.

Flight from different parts of the body

Large apparatus

• Ask the children to climb on to the climbing frame and swing off from either their hands or one hand and one foot and land on a mat.

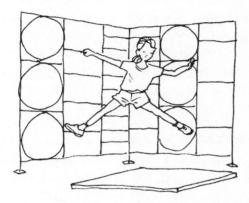

• Ask the children to get on to the apparatus with one or two knees, jump off from two knees on to their feet.

• Ask the children to jump on to the apparatus so that they land on their bottoms. They should then push off from their bottoms and hands and land on a mat.

• Ask the children to roll forwards on to the apparatus. They should then, at the end of the table, roll from their shoulders to dismount.

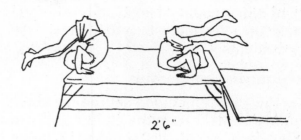

• Ask the children to lie on the bench and take-off by rolling off the bench and then along the mat.

Units of work for Year 5

Unit one: travelling with a partner

Partner activities without contact: matching, mirroring and 'Follow-my-leader'

Skill training

• Arrange the children into pairs and ask one child in each pair to lead her partner around the room. They should walk, skip, jump, jog, run and hop and move in all directions. The children should then make up a movement sequence which they are able to repeat three times.
• Ask the children to stand beside their partners and travel about the room in different directions and in different ways.
• Ask one child in each pair to make up a short sequence showing different travelling patterns in different directions and tell his

103

partner to copy him.

• Arrange the children into pairs and ask them to move away from and towards their partners. They can skip, jump, jog, run and hop. Ask them to move sideways, together or by sidestepping. Finally, they should make up a sequence based on these movements.

Intermediary apparatus

Let the children help to set out benches and mats. Make sure the children stay in their pairs and divide them so that some work on benches and others on mats.

• Ask the children to follow their partners over, on, and around their apparatus.

• Ask them to make up a movement sequence, whereby they work side by side with their partners. They can move forwards, backwards, towards and away from each other. They might also turn their backs on each other.

Using a partner as an obstacle

Skill training

Arrange the children into pairs and work on the following skills.

• Ask the children to jump over their partners and then kneel down low on the floor while their partners jump over them.

• Ask one child in each pair to make a bridge on the floor.

The other child in each pair should then find different ways of moving over and under the 'bridge' and perhaps through the spaces between her partner's arms and legs.

Encourage the children to change the shape of their bridges so that their partner is challenged into finding new ways to move over and under them.

• Suggest that one child in each pair moves slowly and does, for example, a stretched roll, a curled sideways roll, crawls or moves on her stomach, and that the other child jumps over the moving 'obstacle'.

• Ask one child in each pair to move about on, or around, the spot and the other child in each pair must try to move under them as they keep changing their shape.

Intermediary apparatus

Let the children help you put out some mats and then ask them to each share a mat with a partner. They should work together on the mat, using their partner as an obstacle in the same way as they practised on the floor, but trying to avoid each other by going under, over or around their partner. The mat will give them the confidence to be more daring, to move more quickly and try out different kinds of rolls.

Copying a partner's sequence

Skill training

• Encourage the children to practise balancing positions, different methods of travelling around the room and different take-offs and jumps.

• Ask the children to create a simple movement sequence which they can repeat three times.

• Ask the children to work with a partner and practise working together to perform identical sequences.

Large apparatus

Encourage pairs of children to choose their own apparatus on which to make up a combined movement sequence. This will enable each pair to work at their own ability level. The teacher should guide the children's choice of apparatus and, as always, make sure that the layout is safe for each pair to be active.

Unit two: balance

Supporting and transferring body weight

Skill training

Encourage the children to practise their balances.

Intermediary apparatus

Set out, with the children's help, benches and mats and let the children work on the following movement tasks.
• Revise with the children all the balances which they have tried on the floor and ask them to try them on the bench.
• Remind the children about the balances which they can make between the bench and the floor, and let them practise them. For example:

• balancing with two feet on the bench;

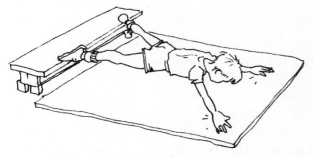

• balancing with two hands on the mat in a star shape;

• balancing with two hands on the mat in a streamlined shape with the head either facing the mat or facing the ceiling;

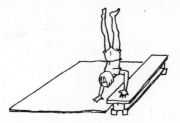

• balancing in a handstand with one hand on the mat and one hand on the bench;

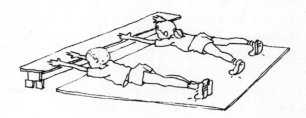

• balancing with two hands on the bench and the toes of both feet on the mat in either a streamlined or star shape.

Ask the children to get on to the benches and straight into balanced positions; for example on one foot, knee, or on their bottoms. Can they then transfer their body weight so that they hold new balanced positions on the mats?

Stress the importance of transferring body weight carefully from one position to another and of making clear shapes.

Stepping into and out of balances

Skill training

Let the children choose activities from the following list:
• Balance on one foot, and then step into a balance on the other foot.
• Balance on two feet and then step into a balance on two hands and one foot.
• 'Cartwheel' by balancing on two feet, stepping on to one foot, one hand, the other hand and one foot.

Draw chalk circles on the floor to help the children cartwheel.

The children can choose from which side to start. If the child starts from '1' he should stand with his back to the circles then put his right foot in circle 1, his right hand in circle 2, his left hand in circle 3 and his left foot in circle 4.

• Balance on one foot and then balance on bottoms, moving into a balance on shoulders and then finally return to standing.

• Free choice of an action which takes the body from a balance or into a balance with stepping action.

Twisting and balancing

Skill training

• Ask the children to balance on two feet, twist their bodies and put their weight on their hands (and if necessary one foot).

• Tell the children to balance on their shoulders with their knees bent. They should then twist their hips and put their knees on the ground and balance in their new positions.

• Ask the children to balance on their stomachs. They should twist their hips and balance on their backs.

• Ask the children to balance on their bottoms. Ask them to twist round until they can balance on their knees.

• Encourage the children to put their weight on their knees and then twist to take their weight on their shoulders.

• Ask the children to make up a sequence of movements which will take them into and out of three balanced positions with a twist. The children may like to use a mat for this activity. Remember to ask children to demonstrate preliminary and finalised

sequences, as examples for the rest of the group. This will increase both their observation skills and their knowledge of particular gymnastic skills.

Show examples of children's movements across the whole range of physical ability. A child with special needs might make up a simple, yet effective, sequence which contains both variety and good shapes, and which answers the movement task set.

Rocking into and out of balances: 1

Skill training

• Ask the children to each balance on one knee, and then rock along one side of their bodies, so that they end up balancing on their shoulders. Can they then rock from their shoulders to their feet?

• Ask the children to rock backwards, from a balanced position on their feet to a balanced position on their shoulders.

Intermediary apparatus

Tell the children to help you lay out mats so that they can work on the following movement tasks.

• Ask the children to practise, on a mat, rocking from their knees to their shoulders, their shoulders to their feet and their feet to their shoulders again.

• Ask the children to see if they can balance on their knees and then rock down the front of their bodies to balance momentarily on their chests.

• Ask the children to balance on one or both of their feet and then rock down the side of their bodies on to a balance on one or both shoulders.

• Let the children try out different balances

and other ways of working into and out of them, for example, working from their knees to their bottoms to their knees, or from their feet to their shoulders to their feet again and so on.

Jumping into and out of balances

Skill training

• Ask the children to balance on one foot and then jump on to the same foot and make a new balanced position.
• Tell the children to balance on one foot, making an interesting shape and then jump on to the other foot and make the same shape again. Can they repeat the same action?
• Ask the children to each jump from two feet on to one foot and hold a good balanced shape.
• Tell the children to stand on two feet, jump and turn around in the air and when they land hold their bodies still.
• Tell the children to stand with their legs and arms wide apart and then jump into the air, keeping their bodies in a star shape. Can they do a half turn in the air?
• Encourage some of the children to try jumping from two feet to two hands (cat-springs).

Intermediary apparatus

Let the children help you set out benches and then work on the following movement tasks.
• Ask the children to jump on to a bench and hold a balance on one or two feet.
• Ask the children to run along the bench and jump into the air and land without moving forwards.
• Ask the children to practise the activities they did on the floor on the benches.

Rocking into and out of balances: 2

Skill training

If the children are to rock their bodies, then their body weight has to be transferred on to rounded surfaces. They should, therefore, practise rocking on various parts of their bodies; for example:

• on their feet, from their heels to their toes or from side to side;
• on their bottoms, from side to side or forwards and backwards;
• on their shoulders, from side to side;
• from their upper to lower backs;
• from their chests to their stomachs;
• obliquely from their shoulders to their hips.

Ask the children to hold their positions from time to time and discuss with them which body parts are easiest to rock on.

Large apparatus

Lay out the apparatus as shown below and ask the children to work on the following movement tasks after they have been allowed to explore the apparatus first.

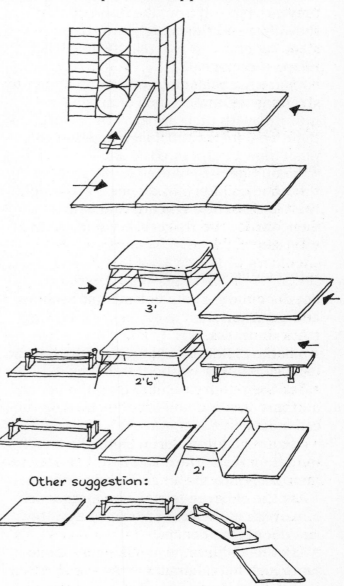

Other suggestion:

• Can the children find places on the apparatus where they can balance?
• Can they find places where they can rock into and out of a balance?
• Can they find places where they can jump into a balance or out of a balance?
• Ask the children to make up a sequence showing different ways of getting into and out of two or three balanced positions.

Unit three: flight

The action of flight: take off, flight position and landings

Skill training

Revise with the children the different ways they can take off from the floor, so that they lift their bodies high into the air.
• Let the children practise the five basic jumps (see page 92).
• Encourage the children to jump higher by stressing the importance of driving upwards with their arms, as they work their feet, ankles and knees together to push their bodies into the air.
• Encourage the children to lift parts of their bodies high into the air, for example their knees, chests, heads and hands.
• Encourage the children to jump as far as they can.

Intermediary apparatus

Let the children help you set out benches and mats and then work on the following movement tasks.
• Ask the children to jump over the bench from side to side without touching it.
• Tell them to try to jump over the bench and turn in the air before they land on the other side.
• Ask the children to run along the bench until they reach the end when they should jump high into the air and land on the mat.
• Ask the children to run along the bench, jump high in the air and turn so that they land facing the bench.
• Ask the children to run along the bench, jump high in the air and make a shape before they land.

108

• Tell the children to run along the bench and jump off sideways into the air and land sideways on the mat.

Large apparatus

Set out the apparatus as suggested below. Let the children explore their apparatus before introducing them to the following movement tasks.

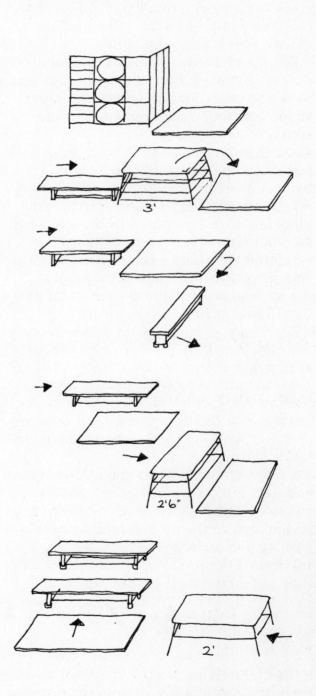

• Ask the children to find different ways of jumping on to, over and off the various pieces of apparatus.

• Let the children choose an apparatus arrangement to work on and make up a movement sequence to show different flight patterns. For example, they might use different parts of their bodies to initiate the flight, or make different body shapes in the air, or they might try taking off from body parts other than their feet.

Units of work for Year 6

There are four units of work in this section. The first unit is divided into three sub-themes which are based on the gymnastic skills which the average child in Year 6 should be able to attempt. The second unit is centred around a more detailed analysis of the shape of the body during gymnastic movement. The third consists of two sub-themes which are centred around a more concentrated study of partner work, while the final unit is structured to enable children to practise and demonstrate the combined gymnastic activities which they should be capable of achieving having reached the end of Key Stage 2.

Unit one: gymnastic skills

Most children are capable of performing seven specific skills at this stage: running, jumping, a forward roll, a backward roll, a headstand, a cartwheel, and a handstand.

Running

The skill of running in a straight line should be taught during athletic activities, but it is necessary to teach children how to run efficiently when they approach a piece of apparatus in order to mount it. The children will need to know how fast to run, and how to control the speed which has been generated to effect a dynamic take-off.

Skill learning

Line the children up in groups of four and let them spring across the length of the hall and jump over a hoop lying on the ground, starting with the first child in each group.

Encourage the children to run on the balls of their feet, lifting their knees high, extending their ankles and keeping their toes pointing in the direction of the hoop. They should also use their arms to drive their legs forward. They should bend their elbows (at an angle of about 90°) point their finger tips at the hoop.

Watch the children as they run and tell them to lean their bodies slightly (70°) and to lengthen their strides.

Intermediary apparatus

Ask the children to help you set out the mats, they should then each run towards a mat in a straight line, take-off and land on the mat.

Large apparatus

Let the children help you set out stacking tables and then tell them to run in a straight line towards the tables, take-off and reach forward to put their hands on them, lifting their legs so that their feet or knees land on top of the apparatus.

Rolling

Skill training

Ensure that the children understand the importance to rolling of holding their bodies in rounded shapes by regulating the tension in their muscles. Then let them try the following rolls across the floor:
• a stretched sideways roll – tell the children to keep their legs and arms off the floor and roll around their lower trunks;
• a tucked sideways roll.

Intermediary apparatus

Encourage the children to practise different rolls. Those children who would like to be retaught how to do a forward or a backward roll correctly should be given assistance.

Balancing

Skill training

Let the children practise balancing on different body parts so that they become aware that the balance position depends on how their bodies are moved into place.

Once the children have taken up a position, they should practise making a clear body shape by extending their legs or arms, their necks and their spines and then holding their positions rigid. Let the children each practise balancing on:
• two heels;
• their lower legs;
• one forearm and one foot;
• one foot;
• one hip.

Intermediary apparatus

Encourage the children to practise a shoulder balance, a headstand and a controlled handstand (with teacher support).

   Some children may not want to try out these specific skills and can, instead, be encouraged to try out balances on other parts of their bodies. For example, they could try balancing in a 'v' shape while sitting. To do this they should place their body weight on to a small part of their bottoms and extend their arms and legs into the air with out letting their feet and hands touch each other.

Unit two: body shape

Symmetry and asymmetry: 1

Skill training

• Ask the children to make symmetrical and asymmetrical shapes while they balance, in turn, on two feet, their shoulders, backs, stomachs, bottoms, knees and hands.

• Tell the children to make symmetrical and asymmetrical shapes while moving on their feet, hands and feet, and their hands and knees. Remind them of the seven gymnastic skills and ask them whether or not each skill can be performed in a symmetrical shape.
• Ask the children to move about the floor and lift different parts of their bodies as high as they can in the air. Are their body shapes symmetrical or asymmetrical?

Intermediary apparatus

Ask the children to help you set out some benches and let them work on the following movement tasks.
• Ask the children to move along or over a bench making symmetrical and asymmetrical body shapes.
• Can the children demonstrate a symmetrical movement and an asymmetrical balance somewhere on the bench?
• Ask the children to make a sequence that incorporates an asymmetrical movement, a symmetrical balance and an asymmetrical jump.

Symmetry and asymmetry: 2

Skill training

Take the children through a warm-up and then remind them about the work which they covered in the previous lesson. It is not necessary to give them any specific skill training, either on the floor or on intermediary apparatus, since the main aim of this lesson is to allow the children to begin to apply their knowledge of symmetry and asymmetry to work on the large apparatus.

Large apparatus

Set out the apparatus as suggested opposite and let the children explore the apparatus.

   Once the children have familiarised themselves with the apparatus, ask them to move across, under, around and off the apparatus showing symmetrical and asymmetrical balances, movements and

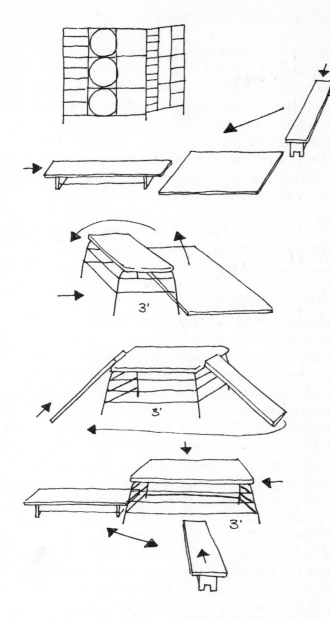

jumps. Emphasise the different actions which can be performed on the climbing frame such as hanging from different parts of the body, inverting shapes, climbing patterns and balancing positions.

Unit three: partners

Mirroring and cannon

Skill training

Arrange the children into pairs and ask them to face their partners. One child in each pair should move her arms and legs at various levels and the other one should mirror her movements.

• Arrange the children into pairs and ask one child in each pair to move across the floor. The other child must watch carefully and then copy.

• Ask the children to make up movement sequences based on the previous two activities.

Large apparatus

Let the children choose and set out whichever apparatus they would like to work on and ask them to plan a movement sequence with their partners based on the skill training activities.

Matching and shadowing: 1

Skill training

The children should each work with a partner and choose movements which they can perform simultaneously. Ask them to compose a sequence of matching movements to include flight, rotation, balance and changes of speed. They can choose to walk beside, behind or facing their partners or use all three positions at various points in the sequence. Let the children work on mats if they require them.

Matching and shadowing: 2

Skill training

Let the children practise the sequences which they composed in the previous matching and shadowing session.

Large apparatus

Let the children choose and set out the apparatus they would like to work on and ask them to compose a sequence of matching and shadowing movements which include balance, rotation and inversion.

Counterbalancing partner's weight

Skill training

• Ask the children to shake hands with a partner. They should hold their partners' hands tightly and lean away so that they are relying on their partners' weight to remain stable. They can try this facing their

partners and standing at the side of their partners.
• Ask the children to hold on to their partners' wrists and lean away.
• Ask the children to lock elbows with a partner and try to push him away.
• Tell the children to hold a partner under both elbows and try to lift her.
• Ask the children to help their partners to make turning jumps.
• Ask the children to help their partners bend over backwards, so that they touch the floor with their hands. Tell the children to pay particular attention to the position of their feet in relation to their partners' feet and body positions.
• Ask the children to sit back to back with their partners and slowly stand up together. They can each compose a sequence with their partners in which they can include various movements of their own choice. However, they must be in contact with their partners throughout the sequence.
• Let the children experiment with the notion of counterbalance. They can be encouraged to sit down, lie down, kneel down and find other ways of working with their partners' support.

Unit four: combined activities

Child-initiated movement sequences

Skill training

• Ask the children to compose a sequence which contains three different bridge shapes. Can they move in one of the bridge shapes? They should find linking movements to move from one shape to another.
• Ask the children to compose a sequence which includes symmetrical and asymmetrical body shapes in flight, stillness and rotation.
• Ask the children to compose a sequence which includes a stretched shape, a twisted shape and a curled shape. Make sure they work at different levels and speeds.

Intermediary apparatus

Let the children help you set out some mats and benches. They can then use the floor or the mats to practise moving with their feet. They should use them together and apart. Some children will choose to practise cartwheels and handstands while others may choose various kinds of rolls.

Using the benches, ask the children to practise making bridges and balances showing symmetrical and asymmetrical shapes. They should move over, along and off the bench showing a variety of arm and leg shapes in the air.

Large apparatus

The following movement tasks can be written out on separate cards so that the children can choose which task they would like to work on. Encourage them to discuss with you which pieces of apparatus might be suitable and how they can be arranged and which movements might be used.
• Ask the children to practise hanging and balancing in various body positions on the climbing frame. Can they find suitable movements to link these positions into a sequence?
• Ask the children to compose a sequence which includes an inverted balance on or against the apparatus, a roll and movements on hands and feet.
• Ask the children to use their hands to vault over a piece of apparatus.
• Tell the children to compose a sequence which includes a symmetrical shape made both on the apparatus and in the air.
• Ask the children to choose balances which they can perform on the apparatus, and link them together to create a sequence.
• Tell the children to compose a sequence of movements which include a turning movement and a twisting movement.

Evaluation sheet
Gymnastics Key Stage 2

	Name							
• Repeat the same series of movements on different occasions:								
Floor								
Apparatus								
• Run up to mount apparatus								
• Jump, land and roll								
Floor								
Apparatus								
• Other skills: Co-operative								
Creative								
Leader								
Understands information								
Able to evaluate performances								
Can lift, carry and manoeuvre apparatus								
Can plan apparatus layouts								
Good body tension in floorwork								
Good body tension on intermediary apparatus								
Good body tension on large apparatus								
Performs the 5 basic jumps								

	Name							
Bunny jump with good hip lift								
Bunny jump over a bench								
Balance on one foot for 60 seconds								
Forward roll								
Match partner's movements – floor								
Match partner's movements – apparatus.								
Balance on small body parts								
Backward roll								
Crouch jump to mount apparatus								
Gains height, single take-off – floor								
Jumps and gets flight from apparatus								
Climbs and descends confidently								
Hangs upside down from apparatus								
Swings on and from apparatus								
Forward roll on to mat from apparatus								
• Advanced skills:								
Headstand								
Cartwheel								
Handstand								
Cat-spring								
Handstand with forward roll								
Backward roll into handstand								
Forward roll on to apparatus								
Backward roll from apparatus								
Vault over 2'6" table								

Chapter 7
Games

'Pupils should, individually, with a partner and in small groups:

• explore and be guided to an understanding of common skills and principles, including attack and defence, in invasion, net/wall and striking/fielding games;

• be helped to improve the skills of sending, receiving and travelling with a ball for invasion, net/wall and striking/fielding games;

• be given opportunities to develop their own games practices, working towards objectives decided sometimes by themselves and sometimes by the teacher;

• make up, play and refine their own games within prescribed limits, considering and developing rules and scoring systems;

• develop an understanding of and play games created by the teacher as well as small sided, simplified versions of recognised games covering invasion, net/wall and striking/fielding games' (Programme of Study).

Games are part of our national heritage and have, over the centuries, become a major feature of our recreational lives. Inevitably, therefore, they form an essential part of any physical education programme. Through the skills needed to play them and the competition brought about by playing them, games can offer children a wide range of educational experiences. However, if these opportunities are to be explored to the full, it will be necessary to ensure that a balanced approach is taken to the teaching of games. In other words, children must not only learn about the full range of games available, but also explore their interrelationship as well as the tactics and principles of play. The foundations for this need to be laid in the primary school, so that children can move smoothly towards learning more specific games and tactics later on in their school lives.

The DES document, *Physical Education for ages 5 to 16* (1991), subdivides games into three main categories:
• invasion games, such as basketball, football and hockey;
• net/wall games, such as badminton, tennis and volleyball;
• striking/fielding games, such as cricket, rounders and stoolball.

Within these categories, each group of games have common principles of play although they may differ in detail according to the game being played.

Throughout the primary years, it is important that children are encouraged to develop their own personal competence in all three categories as this will increase their enjoyment when playing games. Consequently, in the primary years, children should be allowed to experience as many different games as possible centred around the common principles. For example, they will need constant practice using a variety of bats and balls of all shapes and sizes to become skilled, secure and confident in sending, receiving and travelling with a ball or with an implement such as a bat, stick or racquet. It is also important to be aware that the technical expertise which is required to play most games in a competitive situation is extremely demanding. In fact, most children of this age would find it very difficult to compete successfully in many games which are often identified as our 'national games', for example hockey, rugby, cricket and football. Therefore, it is often necessary to modify games so that all children have the chance to take part actively and successfully. The 'case' for the teaching of games is succinctly put by the DES in *Physical Education for ages 5 to 16* (1991): 'A balanced games programme should also contribute towards a pupil's social and cognitive development by providing opportunities for co-operation, competition, problem solving and decision making.'

This chapter is divided into two sections. The first section is intended to be used with children in Years 3 and 4, while the second section is aimed at Years 5 and 6.

Programmes of study for Years 3 and 4

This section is structured to incorporate the programme of study for games in Key Stage 2, and to enable pupils to work towards reaching the end of Key Stage statements (a) to (f). The section provides a progressive programme of study and each lesson follows the format:
• three to five minutes of warm-up;
• ten to fifteen minutes of skill training;
• ten to fifteen minutes of game- related activities;
• two minutes of cool-down.

The work completed in the games activities in Key Stage 1 will have given the children ample opportunities to practise running, chasing, dodging and changing direction. This practice will have helped them to become agile, alert and controlled in their use of space. They will also have had plenty of experience using balls of different sizes, and they ought to be ready to build on the experience they have gained in throwing, catching, kicking and travelling with a ball.

The children should now be ready to practise controlling a ball or shuttle using a variety of implements and incorporating the skill of striking. This will enable them to play a variety of games.

Warm-up activities

Each lesson must begin with a warm-up session and the following warm-up activities are appropriate for all games lessons at this level. Choose a selection from the list according to the children's needs.

Basic warm-ups

- Ask the children to jog around the area and stop when you blow a whistle.
- Ask the children to run around the area and stop when you blow a whistle. They should then change from running to hopping around the area.
- Tell the children to jump from side to side and from their right feet to their left feet.
- Tell the children to jump 20 times on the spot, making sure that they keep both their feet together.
- Ask the children to run, as fast as they can, across a distance of 15–20m.
- Ask the children to jump on the spot. When you give the command 'change' they must all jog around the area.
- Encourage the children to run around the area, when you call a number the children should group together according to the number you call.
- Ask the children to jog on the spot, jog forwards, jog on the spot again and so on.
- Ask the children to jog around the area and when you give the command to change they should choose to either skip, run, hop, gallop or sidestep instead.
- Ask the children to jog around the area and when you blow your whistle, they should bend down and touch the ground and then continue jogging.
- Ask the children to face you and move in the direction which you tell them to, for example backwards, forwards, to the right or to the left.
- Ask the children to sprint around the area and when you blow your whistle, they should jump in the air, land, stop and then sprint in another direction.
- Tell the children to bound across the area with long strides.
- Tell the children to walk across the games area, pivot and return to their starting places. They should then try skipping, jumping and sprinting across.
- Organise practices for the following basic footwork skills: acceleration and deceleration; sudden changes of direction while running; running and stopping suddenly; sidestepping and slip-stepping with frequent changes of direction.
- Organise some balance practices, for example running at speed, jumping into the air, landing and thrusting the right foot forwards to act as a brake. The children should bend their right knees as they land and hold their bodies still.

The children can then do the same, but this time count up to two before they put their left feet on the ground. Can they hold their left feet up until you tell them to put them down?

Tag games

- Ask each child to tuck a coloured band into his waist band. The children must then chase each other and try to collect as many bands as possible.
- Arrange the children into pairs and tell them to face their partners. This time the children should only try to collect their partners' bands.
- Choose one child to chase the other children and try to touch one of them. The two children must then chase as a couple until they catch another child. The game continues in this way until there is only one child left. This child is declared the winner.
- Organise three pairs of children to chase the rest of the class. When these pairs touch another child, they should change places. The aim of the game is to try and stay 'free' for as long as possible.
- Play the game 'Fox and geese'. Tell the children to form teams of four. Ask three of the children in each team, the geese, to hold each other round their waists. The child at the back of the line should tuck a coloured band into her waistband. This is the goose's tail. The fourth child is the fox and must face the line of three. The fox must try to catch the tail. If he succeeds, he should join the front of the line and the child with the tail becomes the fox.
- Play the game 'Frost and sun'. Give three children blue bands to wear. They must then chase the other children and try to touch them. If a child is touched, she must stand still with her legs wide apart as if

frozen. Any child who has not been 'frozen' can 'melt' and free a frozen child by crawling through her legs. The last three children to be touched are declared the winners and they become the new 'frost'.
• Ask the children to form groups of four. Three of the children in each group should hold hands and make a circle and one of them should wear a braid like a tail. The fourth child should stand outside the circle and try to take the braid.
• Choose one child to be the chaser. The chaser must try to touch the rest of the children on different parts of their bodies. Wherever a child is touched they must hold that part and become chasers too. The last child to be touched is the winner.

Arm and body activities

• Ask the children to circle each of their arms in turn.
• Ask the children to lift each shoulder upwards as far as possible.
• Tell the children to jog around the area and when they hear you blow your whistle they must stretch their arms up high.

• Ask the children to clap their hands behind their backs and then in front of their bodies alternately.
• Ask the children to stretch one arm high above their heads and stretch that side of their bodies until their fingers reach as far as possible above their heads.
• Ask the children to make a whole turn and touch the ground. They should then turn round the other way and touch the ground again.

Skill training and game-related activities

The activities in this section are offered as a progressive scheme of work and are intended to cover most of the basic skills with which the children will need to become familiar if they are to enjoy playing games. The activities are related to certain aspects of popular games and each activity and practice includes a real game context in which to practise the skills.

Invasion games

Sending and receiving practice 1: netball and basketball

Ask the children to work with partners on the following activities.
• Ask them to throw large balls underarm with one hand and then underarm with two hands so that their partners can catch the balls. Encourage the children to vary the height of their throws.
• Ask them to continue throwing the balls to their partners, but this time choosing a part of their partners' bodies at which to aim. The children should be ready to bend down or reach up to catch the balls.
• Ask them to throw the balls underarm letting them bounce before their partners catch them.
• Ask them to throw the balls to their partners using an underarm pass and then run to new places and be ready to catch the balls when they are returned.
    Encourage the children to put their

weight on their front feet as they begin to pass the balls, and to watch the flight of the balls as they come towards them when they are receiving them. The children should relax their hands and wrists as they reach out to catch the balls and should use their arms and hands to draw the balls into their bodies.

Game: circular passing rounders

Divide the children into four teams. Each team should form one side of a square, with everybody standing so that they face the centre. Choose one child from each team to stand in the middle of the square, facing their own teams. These children must each feed the ball, by passing it underarm, to each person in their teams. When the last person in each team has received the ball, they should run around the three sides of the square and take their places at the front of their teams and take the first pass of the new sequence. The game continues until everyone has had a turn at running around the square.

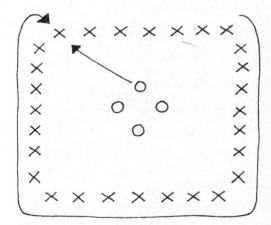

Sending and receiving practices 2: netball and basketball

Teach the children to make a chest pass. They should hold the balls in both hands and spread their fingers across so that their fingertips face upwards and the backs of their hands face their chests. Ensure that their thumbs point towards each other and their arms are bent with their elbows

pointing away from their bodies. Once they are holding the ball in the correct position, they should step forward on one foot and thrust their hands and arms forwards and outwards to throw the balls.

Having grasped the basic technique the children can practise and refine the skill.
• Ask the children to use a chest pass to throw a ball to a partner, aiming at their partners' chests. They should start off by throwing the balls over a distance of about 3m and increase it gradually to 6m.
• Ask the pairs of children to join up and practise throwing the ball between four. Encourage them to pass the ball and then run to a new position, so that they practise the throw-and-run situation they will eventually be required to use in games.

Game: two versus two

Ask the children to work as two pairs in groups of four. One couple must try to pass the ball between them and the other couple must try to intercept the passes and steal possession of the ball. The children should count how many successive passes they make before they loose possession.

Sending and receiving skills 3: netball and basketball

Revise throwing overarm with the children (see pages 48–49). Then proceed with the following activities.
• Ask the children to work with a partner and practise throwing and catching a ball.
• Ask one child in each pair to act as the catcher and stand with one arm outstretched, ready to move. The other child can then throw the ball overarm aiming at the catcher's hand.
• Give each child a ball and let them practise throwing them forward and high into the air. They should then sprint after the balls, jump to collect them, bringing them into their bodies, before controlling their landings.
• Give each child a ball and let them bounce them on the ground and catch them. Show them how to shape and spread their fingers and palms of both hands as they push the balls down towards the

ground. They should relax their wrists, so that they are ready to receive and absorb the impact of the rising balls. When they catch the balls they should place both hands under them and use their fingers to grip and control each catch.

• Let the children work in pairs sending balls to their partners with a one-handed, directed bounce. Make sure that the children are aware that they need to angle their hand on the balls from behind, in order to send them on a diagonal projection. You can try placing a hoop midway between each pair to act as a target to assist the aiming procedure.

Once the children can be seen to complete this successfully, they should be encouraged to bounce balls to their partners and then move to new places to receive the returned balls.

Game: bombardment

Divide the class into two teams and line each team up side by side, facing the other team across a distance of about 10m. Place three balls between the teams, making sure that they are equidistant from both teams. Give each child a large ball and ask them to throw them overarm at the balls in the middle. They must try to move the balls towards the opposing team. If a ball reaches a team it goes out of play and the team who knocked it score a point.

The game is restarted when all three balls go out of play and the team with most points wins.

Travelling with the ball 1: basketball

• Give each child a ball and ask them to practise bouncing them on the spot. They should practise with both hands, and see whether they can vary the height of the bounce and the distance they can bounce the balls away from their bodies.

• Ask the children to stand still and, keeping their hips still, bounce the balls around their bodies.

• Tell them to walk around the area, bouncing the balls with their right and left hands.

• Ask the children to walk and bounce balls at the same time. On the command, 'change', they should pivot round and walk in a different direction, while continuing to bounce the balls.

• Ask the children to walk, jog and run while bouncing balls. When you say 'change' the children should stop moving and bounce their balls on the spot.

• Tell the children to walk, run or jog while bouncing balls. They should change direction when you call the commands, 'backwards', 'forwards' and 'sideways'.

Game: relay bouncing

Divide the class into groups of four. Give each child a ball and ask the four children in each group to stand one behind the other, about 1m apart. The first child in each team can then dribble her ball around the members of her team and return to her place again. Each child should do this, until all four players have had their go. The first team to complete this is the winner. The game can be varied by varying the positions in which the groups stand.

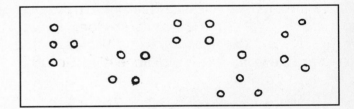

Game: passing

Divide the class into groups of eight (two teams of four) or six (two teams of three) and give each group a ball. The object of the game is to gain possession of the ball and make as many passes as possible before the opposing team gains possession. The children can make up their own rules concerning what they think might be necessary to ensure fair play.

Ask the children to create a game which involves dribbling and pass-bouncing. They can use as many balls as they want and in addition they can use markers and cones.

Travelling with the ball 2: football

• Ask the children to dribble balls using the insides and outsides of their feet. They should keep the balls near to their feet, touching them lightly to move them forward. They should move slowly to begin with and then build up speed and work with a partner, dribbling and passing the balls. Each pair should stand a short distance (3–4m) apart. One partner should then dribble the ball up to the other and then back to where she started.
• Ask the children to choose partners and take turns to dribble around each other.
• Ask the children to work in pairs. One child in each pair should stand with his legs apart and the other should dribble the ball and push it through her partner's legs. She must then collect the ball, with her feet (from behind her partner), and dribble it back to where she started from.
• Put out lots of cones and obstacles or divide the class into two groups and ask one group to be the obstacles. The children should then practise dribbling around the various obstacles. When doing this they should ensure that their feet stay in contact with the ball when they have to look up to find a space to move in to and that they flex their knees when they change direction.

Game: channeling

Divide the class into teams of five children and give each child a ball. Arrange the teams so that, with the members of each team standing side by side, they face another team across a distance of 3m.

Give each child a number and when you call a number the appropriate children should dribble their balls down the 'channel' between the two teams, and then around and behind their own team and back down the channel to their own place. You should watch out for the quickest child each time and declare him the winner.

Sending and receiving skills 1: football

• Ask the children to choose partners and practise passing balls to them. They should use the insides of their feet, and try to remember to send the balls with each of their feet alternately. When they have practised this ask them to try placing their non-kicking foot alongside and level with the ball as they move forward to kick it. Tell them to put their heads over the balls and keep moving forward as they kick.
• Ask the children to practise kicking balls using the outside of their feet.
• See how many times the children can pass and receive balls without losing control. You should help individual children where necessary. When receiving a ball, the child should keep his body weight evenly balanced and reach forward with one foot to meet the incoming ball. As he makes contact, he should relax his legs and absorb the inpact, bringing his feet behind the ball.
• If there is a wall available, ask the children to practise kicking and receiving balls by themselves.
• Ask the children to form pairs and then practise sending a ball to their partners as they both move across the area. The ball should be sent ahead of their partners.
• Let the children remain in their pairs and ask one child in each pair to dribble the ball while the other child sprints on ahead ready to receive it and pass it back again.
• Tell the pairs of children to practise passing balls to each other. However, the balls must pass through two markers which should be placed 1m apart and 5m away from each player. The children should place their feet so that they are at right angles to the space between the markers.

Games

• How many times can two children pass a ball to each other in 30 seconds?
• Mark out a square area of about 5m × 5m and divide the class into groups of four (two teams of two) to play games of passing and receiving with one team trying to intercept the passes of the other.
• You will need to use a wall in this game. Ask the children to form themselves into teams of four. The members of each team should line up behind each other and the

first child in each team should kick the ball against the wall. The second child in the team should receive it and kick it against the wall again. All four children should kick the ball against the wall until the first child receives the ball again and the game is finished. The first team to complete this are the winners.

Sending and receiving skills 2: rugby

The children will need to be given time to familiarise themselves with an oval-shaped ball so that they feel secure and confident when handling it. Let them pass the ball to each other to get used to its shape and ask them questions so that they become aware of its peculiarities; for example:
• 'Which is the best method of holding the ball?'
• 'Do you need to put your hands in a different place when sending the ball than when receiving it?'
• 'What does the ball do as it moves through the air?'
• 'How are you going to catch it?'
Arrange the children into groups of four, and ask them to stand in a square so that they can then practise passing the ball around the square. If this is successful, ask them to turn their backs to each other and continue passing the ball around the square. They can also practise passing the ball using only one hand.

Encourage the children to look before they pass the ball and to make an effort to aim the ball between the receiver's waist and hips. You could also suggest that they vary the height of their passes, and try leaving the ball to bounce on the ground before catching it.

Finally, ask the children to practise passing the ball diagonally and backwards.

Game: diagonal passing

Arrange the children into groups of three and stand them in a diagonal line 3m apart. The first child in the line should then pass a rugby ball backwards to the second child, who, in turn, passes it backwards to the third child. All three children should then

make a half turn so that the third child can pass the ball backwards to the second child and so on. They should be reminded to pass the ball from the right and left alternately. The first group to complete this process four times is the winner.

Travelling with the ball 1: rugby

• Ask the children to each hold a rugby ball and jog around the area. They should keep both hands on the ball and let their arms move across their bodies as they jog. Tell them to make sudden bursts of speed.
• Ask the children to run for about 10m holding a rugby ball. They should place it on the ground and run back to where they started from. Finally, they should sprint back and collect the ball again.
• Arrange the children into pairs and tell the children in each couple to stand 5m apart. Give one child in each pair a rugby ball and ask them to run as fast as they can towards their partners. At the last minute they should swerve so that they avoid running into their partners and continue running for a further 5m, before putting the ball on the ground.

Games

• Form the children into groups of four and tell them to stand in a line 3m apart. The first child in the line should hold the ball in both hands and run in and out of the other three children in the group until she is at the back of the line. She should then pass the ball to the next child in the line, who passes it along the line until it reaches the new first child and the game is repeated.
• Line up teams of four children as in the previous game, but this time the children must all face forwards. They must also keep their feet still when passing the ball and pass the ball backwards, around their bodies, along the line until the fourth child receives it. The fourth child should run to the front of the line and continue passing the ball backwards, as before, until the first child returns to the front.
• Ask the children to arrange themselves in the same formation as in the previous game. The first child in the line must run to

a marker placed 5m away and touch it and run to the back of his team. He should put both his hands on the hips of the child in front of him, who in turn puts her hands on the hips of the child in front of her and so on. As soon as the child who is now at the front of the line feels hands on his hips he should run to touch the marker and the rest of the children take their hands off each other's hips and the game continues until the first child reaches the front again.

Net game practices

Sending and receiving practices 1: volleyball

• Ask the children to spread their hands wide so that their fingertips are upwards and they are looking at the backs of their hands. Ask them to hold the balls in this way so that they are above their foreheads. They should bend their legs and straighten their arms to send the balls into the air. Ask the children to try and make consecutive volleys into the air. They should keep their arms and wrists flexed to absorb the ball as it comes down.
• Ask the children to each volley a ball up in to the air and then let it bounce on the ground. Tell them to bend their knees and volley it into the air again.
• Can the children volley balls into the air while they walk around the area?
• Ask the children to volley the balls as high as they can. How many times can they clap their hands before the balls bounce?
• Ask the children to volley the balls as high as they can and try to turn around on the spot before the balls bounce.

Game

Tell the children to walk with a partner and try out some volleying practices together. Ask them to show you as many different practices as possible.

Sending and receiving practices 2: short tennis

Children will have had only minimal experience of using a bat and ball during Key Stage 1, since most of them will not have been ready developmentally to acquire batting skills at that stage. They will probably, therefore, need to repeat the familiarisation practices on pages 50–51 before they begin this series of activities. (Make sure that each child has a small ball and bat with a short handle.)
• Ask the children to place the balls on their bats and send them away into the air. Can they now let the balls bounce on the floor and catch them on their bats? Can they catch the balls on their bats as they come down?
• Ask the children to see whether they can bat their balls into the air continuously. Tell them to try and vary the height of the balls as they bat them.
• Ask the children to practise catching the balls on the front faces of their bats and then on the back faces of their bats, practising the action of turning their wrists. Can they send the balls into the air from the back of their bats?
• Tell the children to bat their balls on to the ground and try to make them rebound at waist height. Can they do this three times in a row? Can they bat the balls so that they rebound at different heights? What do they have to do to achieve this?
• Can the children pat the balls on to the ground quickly several times? They should bounce them around their bodies and the area, using both sides of the bat.
• Ask the children to bat the balls up into the air and then down on to the ground. They should twist their wrists to do this, but maintain a firm grip on their bats.
• Let the children practise batting their balls against a wall, both alone and with a partner.

Games

• Divide the children into teams of four and ask the children in each team to take turns to hit a ball against the wall. They should let it bounce for the next child to hit it.
• Arrange the children into pairs and ask them to bat a ball to each other, allowing it to bounce each time. Tell them to count how many successive hits they both make.

• Draw a line or place a skipping rope on the ground and ask pairs of children to make up a scoring game.

• Divide the children into teams of four and ask the children in each team to stand one behind the other. From this formation there are a number of relay games which they can play. For example, they can bat a ball on to the ground or carry the ball on their bats or bounce the ball in the air around their whole team or in and out of the members of their teams. They can also take part in some individual challenges by counting how many times they can pat-bounce a ball with their bats. Let the children think of their own challenges.

Striking and field game practices

Travelling with the ball 1: hockey

Show the children how to grip a hockey stick. Stand in front of the class and ask the children to stand sideways so that their left shoulders are facing you. Tell them to place their sticks on the ground so that the flat sides are facing you. The children should grip the top of their sticks with their left hands and make a 'V' shape between their thumbs and first fingers as if they were shaking hands with the stick. They should grip the sticks with their right hands, starting with their palms facing you and curling their fingers tightly around the sticks. Once the children have practised and are comfortable with the grip they can practise some skill training activities.

• Ask the children to practise lifting and lowering their sticks on to and off the ground using their left hands only.

• Tell the children to practise swinging their sticks to the right and left using their left hands.

• Ask the children to walk around the area making short sharp pushes with their sticks. To do this they will need to flex and extend their wrists, while keeping a firm left hand on their sticks.

• Ask the children to stand still and let them practise gripping the sticks with both hands. They should put their right hands at different heights on their sticks to find which feels the most comfortable and allows most movement.

• Let the children practise tapping small balls away from them with their sticks. They should follow the balls and tap them away again. (Ensure that the children's right hands are half way down their sticks.)

• Ask the children to keep the balls in front of their bodies and travel around the area at different speeds, keeping the balls near their sticks at all times.

Games

• Set out some obstacles about 2m apart and ask the children to dribble their balls along the ground and around the obstacles. How quickly can they do it?

• Arrange the children into groups of three and let each child in the group dribble their ball in a figure of eight around the other two children.

• Still in groups of three, ask two of the children in each group to stand behind each other, about 1m apart, with their legs apart. The third child should then dribble a ball through the legs of both children. When the first child has completed this,

124

she should stand with her legs apart so that another player can practise. All three children in each group should practise dribbling and you could see which group completes the task first.

• Can the children think of another game which would involve dribbling the ball using a hockey stick?

Sending and receiving the ball 2: hockey

Teach the children how to drive a ball with a hockey stick before working on the activities. Remind them how to grip the stick, making sure that they place their right hands just below their left. Tell them to swing their sticks backwards and then forwards so that they contact the ball, stepping forward on to their front feet as they hit it and driving the ball away.

• Ask the children to place the ball on the ground and walk up to it and hit it. How close to the ball do they think they need to be when they hit it?

• Tell the children to do the same again but this time run up to the balls and hit them.

Show the children how to push the ball. They will need to grip the sticks so that their right hands are half way down. They should then, with their feet placed shoulder width apart, place the flat sides of their sticks against the balls and push them away. They will need to use the force from their right shoulders and the right sides of their bodies, stepping forwards on to their right feet as they push the balls away.

• Ask the children to push their balls away, making them go as straight as they can.

• Tell the children to move their feet, shoulders and sticks and practise pushing their balls in different directions. They should chase after their balls each time and continue the practice.

• Tell the children to work in pairs and push and drive a ball to each other.

• Ask the children to tell you how to stop the ball and show you what they have been doing. Where do they think is the most effective place to put their right hands? Which is the best position for their sticks? Is it best to keep their heads over their

sticks and balls? Is the stopping action like catching a ball?

Games

• How far can the children drive a ball? Who can drive one the furthest?

• Place an obstacle such as a cone, about 3m away from the children and ask them to push their balls towards the obstacle and see how many times they can hit it.

• Ask the children to choose partners and push a ball to each other. The partner should stop the ball and push it back again. How many times can the pairs push and stop the ball in 30 seconds?

• Use a wall or a bench turned on its side and ask the children to practice hitting the ball against it so that it rebounds. They should work in pairs, with each partner collecting the ball and returning it. If working indoors you should use a soft ball.

Game: skittle ball

Place two skittles on the playing area so that they are 25m apart. Divide the children so that they are in teams of four and two teams should play against each other. Each team must try to score goals by hitting the opposing team's skittle. When a goal has been scored, the game should be restarted from the centre of the area, with the teams taking turns to make the initial centre pass.

When the children have played the game for a few minutes, ask them if they would like to suggest a rule or rules to implement.

Sending and receiving the ball 3: rounders and cricket

Before the children attempt the activities in this section revise with them the technique of throwing a small ball with an overarm throw (see page 48–49). Once they have gained confidence with this technique they can begin the activities.

• Ask the children to practise throwing their balls high in the air with an overarm throw and then an underarm throw, catching them each time. Tell them to try catching the ball using their right, their left and then both hands.

• Ask the children to vary the height of

125

their throws.
• Tell the children to use an overarm throw and an underarm throw to send their balls as far away as possible. They should chase after them and pick them up.
• Arrange the children into pairs and ask one child in each pair to throw their balls to their partners. Tell them to vary the height and direction of their throws so that their partners are forced to move their feet, and to jump high or bend low to catch the balls. Encourage the receivers to move into the line of the oncoming balls, making a catching cradle with their hands.

Games: 'Piggy in the middle' and 'Chimneys'

• Arrange the children into groups of three and ask them to play 'Piggy in the middle'. Tell the children that they should not throw the ball any higher than stretched arm height.
• Form the children into groups of five and show them how to play 'Chimneys'. Tell the groups to form a circle with one child in each group standing in the middle. This child should throw a ball in the air and call out a player's name. This child must then run and try to catch the ball. Every player has three lives and each time someone misses the ball, she loses a life. The last child to lose all his lives is the winner.

Sending and receiving the ball 4: cricket

Teach the children the bowling action used in cricket. They should hold the ball in their fingers and turn sideways, so that their left shoulders are facing a target point. Tell them to let their right arms hang straight down at the right sides of their bodies and stretch their left arms in the air. They should then take a long step on to their left feet, ensuring that their toes face the target, and as they do so move their left arms down towards their left hips and simultaneously swing their right arms over the top of their heads and release the ball. As they swing their right arms they should

follow through by stepping forward with their right feet. Remember to reverse these instructions for left-handed children and always give demonstrations from your right and then your left sides.

Help the children to improve their technique and ask them to try the following activities.
• Ask them to practise bowling at a target from a distance of 10m.
• Ask them to practise a six step run up to a line followed by the bowling action. They should practise this *without a ball* at first.

Having practised bowling, the children can be given some batting experience. They can use bats of various sizes and shapes. Arrange the children into groups of three and let the children in each group take turns to be the batter, the bowler and the fielder. The bowler should stand about 10m from the batter and bowl the ball underarm so that it bounces on the ground about half a metre in front of the batter. The batter should be ready for the ball, with his bat taken back ready to strike it. When the ball bounces, the batter should move his left foot forward so that it is alongside the ball and bat the ball away. The batter can bat the ball in any direction and the fielder should chase or catch the ball. If the batter is left-handed, then he should move his right foot forward and so on.

Game

Divide the class into groups of six players and set out the players as shown in the diagram below.

Let each player have five turns at batting, trying to score as many runs as possible.

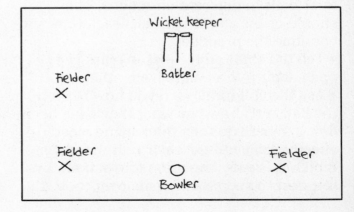

Once a batter has had five goes then all the players should change positions. The player with the most runs at the end of the game is the winner. The fielders should try to get the batter 'out' by catching the ball or bowling at the wicket.

Move about the various groups, reminding players about fielding, catching and bowling techniques.

Ask the children if they would like to introduce any rules; for example, what happens when a fielder catches the ball or if the wicket is hit?

Cool-down activities

The following cool-down activities can be used after any of the sessions in this section. Use them in combination to fill about two minutes.
• Ask the children to walk around the area alternating short strides with long strides.
• Ask the children to take a deep breath. As they breathe in they should raise their arms above their heads and as they breathe out they should bring their arms down to their sides.
• Tell the children to stretch their arms in the air and then stand with good posture.
• Tell the children to walk around the area. Make sure that they hold their bodies in a good posture and tell them to change their direction of travel often.
• Ask the children to follow their partners as they walk around the area.
• Ask the children to use sidesteps, leading with their right legs, to cross the area and then return to their starting positions by leading with their left legs.
• Ask the children to, in turn, jog gently, walk briskly and walk normally.

Programmes of study for Years 5 and 6

The material presented for Years 5 and 6 is based on the traditional games teaching method already known to primary school teachers. This method is centred on a skill learning approach. The skills, however, are not learned in isolation, but are placed firmly in a games context. Therefore, although all the suggested activities and practices which follow are related to known 'major' games (recognised games with governing bodies), they can be experienced through 'minor' games (those games created to develop the skills of major games, such as 'Kwik cricket' and 'New image rugby') or games which are made up and offered at child-interest level.

There are, however, other methods of teaching games, for example through a 'games for understanding' or 'games making' approach. Using this teaching method, the children are encouraged to make up games and thus become involved in solving problems, making and justifying decisions and choosing options.

It is perfectly possible to merge the two teaching methods successfully by blending together the inventing of games, minor games which are related to the recognised major games, and some of the adapted games promoted by the different national governing bodies of sport.

National governing bodies of sport

There is a national governing body for each major game which is played in the United Kingdom. They are responsible for the rules, the coaching, the development and the 'image' of the various games. As well as producing informational literature, each body employs development officers to provide assistance throughout the regions. Any teacher who wants help with teaching a major sport ought to consider approaching the appropriate national governing body for advice.

The national sporting bodies are very much aware of the issues which play a part in teaching games in a primary school; for example, they do not recommend that adult forms of games are played in curriculum time in primary schools. They are aware that the adult versions would not enable children of this age to have enough involvement in the game and that often the children would not have sufficient skill practice either, in the time that is usually available in a lesson. Furthermore, they are acutely aware that every child, regardless of his or her sex, race or ability, has an entitlement, in curriculum time, to be 'games educated'. It is precisely because of such concerns that the various national governing bodies have produced 'small-sided' games such as 'Kwik cricket' and 'Mini hockey' and have even invented new games such as 'New image rugby'. They have also adapted some games by producing 'junior rules' and reducing the number of players needed and the number of rules by which certain games are played. They have also suggested alterations to court and field size. All this has been done with the intention of making the games experience available to *all* children in the primary age range. (A compendium of the national governing bodies of sport, together with references to some of the relevant booklets produced, is given in the Resources section, pages 207–208.)

Lesson structure

The structure for each lesson should be similar to the format suggested for Years 3 and 4 (see page 116). However, as the children reach Year 6, they will be more capable of sustaining the playing of a small-sided game for longer periods. The format for Year 6 might, therefore, more likely resemble the following:
• three to five minutes of warm-up;
• five to seven minutes work on specific skills and games related activities;
• twenty minutes playing the game;
• two minutes of cool-down.

Warm-up activities

The older child will probably enjoy a game-centred warm-up. The following selection of warm-up activities contain some element of game playing.
• Play the tag games as are described on page 117.
• Ask the children to play the 'Bean game' (see page 38).
• Ask the children to jog around the area until you tell them to shake hands with a partner, or clap both hands with a partner, or stand back to back with a partner or bump bottoms. Can the children think of any other actions?
• Use the markings on the games area and send the children to touch various lines and circles. You can then ask them to run, hop, skip and jump to the marks and see who can arrive first.
• Discuss various dodging and feinting routines with the children. Ask them to practise some of them with a partner.
• Gather the children in a restricted space, such as the netball shooting circle, and ask them to jog around the area without touching anyone else.
• Ask the children to run anywhere they like. When you call a number, say three, that number of children should join hands in circles and skip around until you tell them to jog around on their own.
• Ask the children to form themselves into teams of four and jog around the area, one behind the other without touching any other teams. The last person in the team can choose to sprint to the front of the team when he chooses.
• Let the children play 'Follow-my-leader' in pairs and allow the leaders to choose any movements they like until you blow your whistle. At this signal the leaders have ten seconds to try and make as much space between themselves and their partners as they can. You should then blow the whistle and all the children must stand still. If any of the children who are chasing can touch the leaders, they have won and become the new leaders.
• Let them practise skipping with a rope.

Skill training

Choose the most suitable method for introducing the children to skill learning and games playing. You might choose the traditional method, whereby you analyse the game which the children will eventually be required to play and extract those skills which they will need to practise prior to game involvement. You might, however, ask the children to make up a game and then ask them which skills they think they should practise to make the game more enjoyable. For example, if the game you wanted to work towards was a football related game such as 'End ball' (a passing, marking and goal scoring game for two teams of four players) and you were approaching it using the traditional method, you may decide that the skills to be practised would include: dribbling, kicking and aiming, marking, tackling, dodging, passing, intercepting, formation passing, and defending a target.

However, if you were approaching it using the second method you might ask the children to make up a game using large balls and suggest that they use their feet to move the ball about the area. You could supply equipment such as cones and bands, letting the children choose what they need. They might need assistance in organising the game, but they could be encouraged to sort out any problems for themselves by asking such questions as: 'What do you think?' or 'What kind of game are you thinking about?' or 'How do you think you will score points in your game?' and then eventually, 'Are there any skills you would like me to help you with?'

Game playing

The games in this section can be approached using the first method.

Danish rounders: rounders and cricket related

Skills to be practised:
• throwing underarm;
• throwing overarm;
• fielding;
• catching;
• sprinting;
• batting;
• bowling.

Place a number of hoops so that they form the four corners of a square. The distance between the hoops will depend on the skill of the children. Let the children choose a tennis ball or a rounders ball and let them choose any kind of bat. Organise the children so that there is one fielder standing inside each hoop as well as other fielders placed around the area. One child should bowl a ball underarm to the batter who, after batting the ball, should run around the four hoops before the fielders have fielded the ball and passed it from the first hoop to the fourth, via the second and third hoops. If the batter reaches the fourth hoop before the ball, he scores a rounder. If not, he is out. Other rules can be decided by the children; for example, whether someone should be out before if a fielder catches the ball he has batted before it bounces and how far away the bowler should be when she bowls and so on.

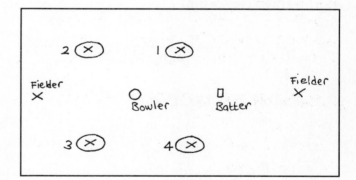

Captain ball: netball and basketball related

Skills to be practised:
• shoulder pass;
• chest pass;
• overhead pass;
• basketball dribble bouncing;
• marking and dodging.

This game is played by two teams of six players. Each team should be divided so that three players are on the playing area, for example a netball court, and three off the playing area. The players who are off the playing area should stand on a bench (or behind a line). Possession is decided initially by throwing the ball up equidistantly between two players, who must jump and gain control. Play starts with a centre pass, and three consecutive passes must be completed successfully by one team before they can score. To score a goal a player must, after three passes, pass the ball to a player standing on the bench. As soon as a goal is scored, the children from both teams on the benches change places with those on the playing area and the game continues with a 'throw up' start.

This game can be adapted so that a basketball dribble is allowed in addition to the three passes.

King ball: netball related

Skills to be practised:
• bouncing and aiming;
• overarm throwing;
• intercepting;
• dodging and marking;
• underarm throwing.

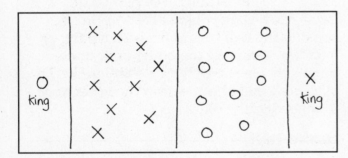

Divide the area with three lines as shown in the diagram and arrange the children into two teams. Pick one child from each team to be 'king' and stand the children on the courts so that the kings stand behind their opponents' teams. Give one team possession of the ball and they should attempt to pass the ball to their own 'king'. Once a 'king' receives the ball he must try to hit one of the opposing team below the knee with it. If he is successful, the player who was hit must go and join his own 'king', when he too can receive the ball and attempt to hit the opposing players. The game should continue until all the players in one team are standing with their 'king',

and the other team are declared the winners.

Discuss with the children the possibility of making up some other rules to ensure fair play and to avoid children hurting themselves.

Skittle ball (see page 125)

This game can be adapted so that it is hockey, basketball or football related. Skills to be practised:
• dribbling;
• stopping the ball;
• passing the ball;
• intercepting;
• shooting;
• dodging;
• tackling;
• marking;
• defending.

Bombardment (see page 120)

Skills to be practised:
• underarm throwing;
• aiming;
• overarm throwing;
• fielding.

The game described on page 120 can be adapted so that it is cricket related by using cricket-sized rubber balls or rounders balls to move the large balls across the area.

French cricket: rounders and cricket related

Skills to be practised:
• aiming;
• throwing overarm;
• throwing underarm;
• batting;
• fielding;
• defending.

Arrange the children into teams of five or six. One child should be given a cricket bat to hold so that she guards her legs. The other players, who may not move when they are in possession of the ball, must then attempt to throw the ball so that it touches the batter's legs. Whoever succeeds is the new batter.

Shooting for invasion games

Shooting at goal is probably the most exciting aspect of any game and children like to score goals. Thus children are usually quite happy to practise shooting as a game in itself. It is quite easy to set up enough football, hockey and new image rugby posts (cones spaced a certain distance apart across an area) for a whole class of children to use at one time, but not so easy to provide enough netball or basketball rings. One way to overcome this problem, is to have a 'round robin' system where groups of children spend a specific amount of time at each activity.

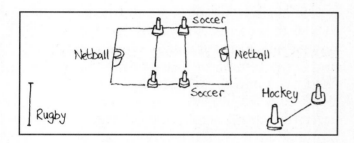

Soccer

The most important point to stress when practising shooting at goal is accuracy. Several practices should be set up which allow the children to practise shooting without encountering any opposition before introducing practices with opposition. The diagram below illustrates several ways to structure practices using groups of three and no opposition.

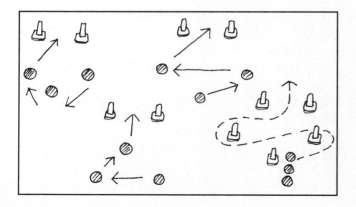

When the children move on to practising with an opposition, use two players against another two players and a goalkeeper. One team should start the attack from about 20m away from the goal line and the two defenders should try and stop their attack.

Rugby

The children should practise moving forwards and throwing the ball backwards in diagonal lines consisting of four people.

They should begin their attack from 30m away from the try line and be encouraged to move at speed and catch accurately. The child nearest the try line at the end of the run should place the ball firmly on the ground.

Netball

Each child should have his own ball and be encouraged to shoot from a position near to the goal post until he can score goals frequently.

As the children become more accurate they can move so that they are one step away, then two, then three and so on. Eventually, they will be able to practise passing the ball to and fro with a partner from the centre of the court until one player receives a ball inside the circle. This player should shoot within three seconds of receiving the ball.

Basketball

Encourage the children to pat-bounce their balls from the centre of the court and shoot as soon as they are inside the shooting area. Encourage them to build up their speed of attack as soon as they are showing some accuracy in scoring goals.

Hockey

Goal shooting practice should proceed as for soccer.

Goalkeeping in soccer and hockey

The skill of goalkeeping is often neglected in games lessons, yet it can also provide the basis for an enjoyable games activity.

Arrange the class into groups of three – one feeder, one goalkeeper and one fielder.

The feeder should send the ball underarm from different angles and different heights. The goalkeeper should reach to the left and to the right at various heights to retrieve the ball.

When practising this in conjunction with soccer the goalkeeper should be encouraged to jump high to retrieve a high ball and be prepared to go on the ground for a rolling ball. The goalkeeper should throw the ball overarm to the fielder so that she can kick it back to the feeder.

If practising goalkeeping in conjunction with hockey, the children should use tennis balls rather than hockey balls and the goalkeeper must keep one hand on his stick throughout the practice. He can use his feet, or his stick to send the ball away from the goal mouth.

Small-sided games

Some teachers are hesitant about setting up several small-sided games in one lesson and prefer instead to play a class game where they can control all of the children all of the time. From a management point of view this is understandable, but this method does not give children the opportunity to become independent nor to practise working together co-operatively. Nor can they have the opportunity to solve the mild disputes which inevitably occur in most game-playing situations. If teachers can be persuaded to allow children to try and solve games problems for themselves, then not only will they be more able to cope with any disputes in lesson time, but they will also be better equipped to sort out disputes in the playground without the presence of the teacher.

A good example of a small-sided game is 'Australian kanga' or 'Kwik cricket'. You would probably have, in this instance, three separate small-sided games in operation at the same time across the school playing field (see above).

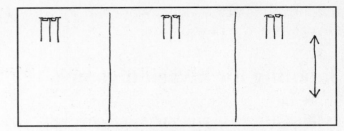

The same organisation could be developed for five-a-side games of soccer, hockey or new image rugby.

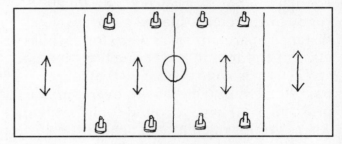

It is not so easy, however, to create an organisational management pattern for a whole class to be involved at the same time in invasion games such as netball and basketball or net games such as volley-ball and short tennis, because of the lack of resources and of suitable surfaces. Whenever possible, therefore, these activities should either be offered alongside a field game or several of the activities should be offered together. For example, for a class of 28 to 30 children you could organise them as follows:
• 14 children playing junior netball and 16 children playing new image rugby (either two teams of eight or four teams of four);
• three teams of four playing short tennis and four teams of four playing Kwik cricket;
• two teams of four playing volley-ball and four teams of five playing soccer;
• two teams of four playing short tennis, two teams of four practising soccer shooting, four children playing badminton and two teams of four playing volley-ball.

It is important to have access to relevant information booklets on small-sided games from the particular governing bodies. These booklets will provide information about how to play each game together with suggestions for skill related practices which are suitable for older primary school children (see Resources section).

Evaluation sheet

Games: End of Key Stage 2 Statements Specific

It is suggested that you agree a graded system of recording this data, such as:

1 = not yet reaching the level required
2 = responding satisfactorily and reaching an acceptable standard
3 = above average
4 = outstanding

Name   Comments

- Able to: plan practice (and) improve more complex games activities

- Responds safely: alone (and) with others to given tasks

- Able to sustain energetic activity

- Understands: the immediate (and) long term effects of exercise on the body

- Is able to evaluate his own (and) his peers' performance.

Activity Specific

- Ability to perform the three fundamental skills (Sending: S, Receiving: R, Travelling: T) as listed:

Football
S Kick accuracy
S Kick distance
R Stop the ball (trap)
T Dribble
S Heading
Netball
R Catch
S Chest pass
S Shoulder pass
S Bounce pass
S Shoot
Cricket
S Bat
S Bowl
S Overarm throw
R Field ball

										Name	Comments

Tennis
S Bat forehand
S Bat backhand
S+R Keep up a rally
S Serve underarm
S Bat (accuracy)
Rounders
S Bat (accuracy)
S Bat (distance)
R Catch
S Throw overarm
S Bowl underarm
R Field
Hockey
S Drive the ball
S Dribble the ball
R Stop the ball
Basketball
S Dribble the ball
S Chest pass
S Shoot
Rugby
R Catch
S Pass (accuracy)
S Pass (distance)
T Running with the ball
S Kick (distance)

• Understanding of common principles/   skills of attack/ defence in all games:

Football
Netball
Cricket
Tennis
Rounders
Hockey
Basketball
Rugby

• Spatial awareness

• Ability to create games

• Ability to keep to rules

Chapter 8
Athletic activities

'Pupils should:
- **practise and develop basic actions in running (over short and longer distances and in relays), throwing and jumping;**
- **be given opportunities for and guidance in measuring, comparing and improving their own performance;**
- **experience competitions, including those they make up themselves'**

(Programme of Study).

'Athletic activities concern the pursuit of the fulfilment of individual potential. Pupils strive to improve performance against measurements and/or others in maximising their performance in terms of time, height, length or distance. Athletic activities build on children's natural capacities to run, jump and throw. They promote all-round physical development – speech, strength, stamina and flexibility.

Through organised events and measurement of achievement, pupils have opportunities to engage in and to manage competition against others, against set standards and against their own previous performance. The nature of competition in athletic activities is different from that of other competitive sports in that the event is predetermined and the nature of the contest is known. In many events the number of variables a competitor can expect to meet is minimal. As a result of the nature of the competition, physical training and development of efficient technique are more important preparation than development of tactics or practice of competitive situations. Athletic activities afford the most obvious example of one to one rivalry in competition, and therefore provide opportunities for learning to cope with such rivalry in a healthy and positive way...' (*PE for ages 5 to 16*, 1991).

Although the inclusion of athletics in the school curriculum is not a new phenomenon for the majority of junior schools, there has always been a wide disparity in its presentation as a subject. As a result, while some schools have introduced specialised athletic programmes for their children, others have merely produced a quick series of lessons meant to be used for some 'major' school event such as an annual sports day.

Perhaps the main reason for this wide variety of thinking and practical implementation lies in the ongoing debate about the desirability of exposing young people to the notion of competition. Those teachers who genuinely care about the issue inevitably find themselves in the classic dilemma – keen to support the needs of high achievers and yet sensitive to the needs of those who perform less well. How do you produce an athletics programme which is all-embracing; in fact, how do you produce one at all?

Ironically, the new proposals for programmes of study for physical education in Key Stage 2 could bring the debate on the desirability of competition for children to an end. Not only must children of junior school age now **'experience competitions'** (Programme of Study), but teachers must also address the important issue of educating children with motor impairments within mainstream schools and ensure that athletic activities and competition are available for them too. There is no room for manoeuvre here. While athletic activities can lead high achievers into a high profile sport, they should also form the basis for *all* children to become involved in health-related fitness programmes for life.

Overall, athletics transmits excellent role models; for example, male and female athletes are given equal status, people from all ethnic backgrounds meet and compete together in different parts of the world and disabled athletes have their own Olympic games. It is hardly surprising that athletics has almost universal appeal.

There are also a number of award schemes available to schools which have helped to promote athletics. The two schemes most widely used in the primary school have been the Ten Step Award Scheme and the ESSA TSB Award Scheme, both of which offer recognition badges for children's achievement (see Resources for contact addresses). As with any commercially produced scheme, it almost goes without saying that teachers should read all the background information about the scheme before trying it out with children. In common with all aspects of the physical education curriculum, it is essential that there should be a sound progressive teaching programme which is appropriate to the age and development of children across the whole ability range. Further, teachers should emphasise effort and improvement in the children's work rather than ability. Children need to be motivated if they are to learn new skills or to improve old ones. They need positive reinforcement in order to protect their self-esteem – the younger they are, the more they need it.

However, since athletics concerns the fulfilment of individual potential, this will inevitably lead to a certain amount of one-to-one rivalry which will undoubtedly present both teachers and children with problems. It is assumed through all the programmes which follow that teachers will help all the children to cope with this rivalry in a healthy and positive way. They should, for instance, praise improvement in each child's performance rather than only praising the person who wins the race or who throws the furthest. The children should, however, be made aware that some people can, for example, throw further because they are stronger and that if they practise their arm strengthening activities then they too might be able to throw equally far, or even further. Also give praise to teams who win games or races in order to stress the co-operative nature of the event.

Teaching programme

This chapter is divided into four sections from which it is possible to select material according to the children's needs. The first section consists of four warm-up schedules. The second section provides a number of strength activities and the fourth section lists a selection of cool-down activities. The central core of this chapter, however, is the third section which contains information on skill training, suggestions for improving performance and some ideas for class activities. The information is presented in developmental order so that it is possible to make a progressive programme for each year group. The children will, of course, need to repeat the basic skill of running throughout the four years, but the skills of jumping and throwing will become more orientated towards 'real' athletic events.

Each athletics lesson which is developed from these sections should have a similar format to all other physical education lessons, but even more care should be taken with the warm-up stage of each lesson.

Section one: warm-up

It is vital that children are thoroughly warmed-up before beginning athletic activities. Junior school children usually work over-enthusiastically and competitively, sometimes beyond their capabilities, and could easily strain a muscle or tear a ligament if they are not warmed-up properly.

Each of the four warm-up schedules which are suggested below are chosen so that each body joint is exercised and so that the children's heart and respiratory rates are increased. You may need to alter the schedules when weather conditions are cold or where extra warming is needed for specific athletic exercises and you should decide how many repetitions of each activity are required.

Warm-up one

• Ask the children to jog around the area slowly and then change so that they are jogging quickly and then slowly again.
• Ask the children to jog around the area and stop suddenly when they hear the command.
• Can the children touch the ground with one hand and then with both hands while still jogging?
• Ask the children to lift their shoulders upwards and downwards. They should lift their right and left shoulders separately and then both together.
• Let the children try to grasp their hands together behind their backs, by putting one arm over their shoulders and the other behind their backs. They should try first putting their right arms over their right shoulders and then putting their left arms over their left shoulders.
• Ask the children to circle their arms from their shoulders. They should swing them separately and then together.
• Ask the children to jog around the area at a medium pace.
• Ask the children to walk around the area taking long strides.
• Tell the children to hop on their right legs and then on their left legs.

Warm-up two

• Ask the children to walk around the area. They should alternate between walking slowly and quickly.
• Ask the children to walk quickly and stop suddenly when they hear the command.
• Tell them to walk with long strides.
• Tell the children to jog slowly, then quickly and then stop.
• Ask the children to alternately hop, skip and stride around the area.
• Ask the children to circle their shoulders.
• Tell them to stretch their arms wide and twist from their waists so that they turn to the right and to the left.
• Let the children jog gently for one minute.
• Tell the children to clasp each knee in turn to their chests.

• Ask the children to circle their ankles first to the right and then to the left.
• Tell the children to use the opposite hands to each of their feet and pull their feet up behind them so that they touch their buttocks.
• Let the children jog and then speed up so that they are running.

Warm-up three

• Tell the children to jog forwards and backwards alternately.
• Ask the children to slip-step to the right and to the left.
• Ask the children to hop, jog, skip, jog and so on, around the area.
• Tell the children to jump up in the air several times, using both feet.
• Can the children make a star jump, a stretched jump and a tucked jump?
• Ask the children to turn their heads gently to the right and hold, and then to the left and hold. Tell them to bring their heads forward and hold.
• Tell the children to stretch their arms wide and move their arms forwards and backwards twisting from the shoulders.
• Ask the children to spread their fingers wide and clench their fists several times.
• Tell the children to clasp their hands behind their necks and push their elbows as far back as they can.
• Tell the children to stretch out their arms and twist their waists to the right and left.
• Let the children jog forwards gently and turn and return to where they started from.

• Encourage the children to lunge forward with each leg in turn, placing their feet so that they are at right angles.
• Ask the children to stretch up high on to tiptoe and then curl back down again.

Warm-up four

• Ask the children to jog in the area. They can then alternate jogging with walking. Tell them to stop suddenly.
• Ask the children to alternate jogging with sprinting and again stop suddenly when you tell them to.
• Tell the children to jog around the area, but they should try to lift their knees as high as they can.
• Tell the children to stand on the spot and take long, lunging strides in each direction.
• Let the children sit down and stretch their legs out in front of them. Encourage them to flex their feet, pointing their toes towards their bodies and then stretch their feet by pointing them towards the ground.
• Tell the children to remain seated and stretch their legs so that they are wide apart. Can they touch their toes?
• Tell the children to hop on their right feet and then their left feet.
• Ask the children to jump around the area keeping their feet together.
• Ask the children to stand with their legs and arms stretched out wide. They should keep their elbows straight and circle their wrists and then circle their shoulders.
• Tell the children to shrug their shoulders.
• Ask the children to circle their arms from

their shoulders. They can circle them forwards and backwards.

• Tell the children to place their hands on their waists and then rotate and straighten one of their arms as if they were throwing something away.

• Can the children touch their hands if they put one of their arms over their shoulders and the other behind their backs?

• Encourage the children to lean back and step backwards. They can also practise a throwing action forwards.

• Show the children how to do press-ups when on their hands and knees.

• Show the children how to do squat thrusts. Tell them to crouch down and then jump and push both legs so that they are stretched out behind them. They should then jump and bring both legs back to their hands, so that they are in a crouched position again.

• Ask the children to practise right and left-hand pulls with a partner.

Section two: strengthening activities

The activities in this section should be included in each lesson so that the children's strength develops and their performance can improve. In Key Stage 2, most of the athletic activities will be centred around the three core areas of running, jumping and throwing. Thus, the following strengthening activities have been divided into three groups.

Several athletic activities will have already been introduced in Key Stage 1. If some of the athletic activities have not been covered or if you would like to repeat Lesson 10 from Key Stage 1, this would be a good starting point for the beginning of the Key Stage 2 programme. It would also allow evaluation of the children's performances.

Running

• Ask the children to hop on the spot using both their left and right legs. How far can they hop on one leg?

• Tell the children to leap from their right feet to their left.

• Ask the children to jump alternately on their left and right legs, lifting each knee up to their chests.

Jumping

• Ask the children to run and jump as high as they can.

• Tell the children to step and thrust off from one of their legs into the air.

• Ask the children to skip. Tell them to lift their knees as high as they can.

• Encourage the children to step off a low obstacle such as a bench and push themselves high into the air.

• Ask the children to leap over low obstacles making sure they keep both feet together.

• Tell the children to jump over low obstacles, but this time they should jump with one foot following the other.

Throwing

• Help the children to do press-ups. How many can they do?
• In pairs, ask one child to stand astride in the overarm throwing stance and take his arm back into the throwing position. His partner should *gently* pull his arm towards her so that he has to lean backwards slightly, but resisting the pull from the second child.

You could also let the children practise some of the strength activities in the gymnastics chapter (see pages 88–91).

Section three: skill training

Skill training should be the focal point of each lesson. The children should be shown the techniques required to improve each athletic skill and be given a variety of practices so that they can enjoy themselves while also acquiring the skill.

Running: the sprint

Remind the children of the correct sprinting technique (see page 58) and let them practise this for a short time. The children can then be shown ways to improve their performances.
• Ask the children to run across the area lifting one of their knees to hip height on each step.
• Set out three cones or markers at 15m intervals and ask the children to run as fast as they can to the first marker, slowly to the second marker and as fast as possible to the last marker.
• Tell the children to run gently, keeping their bodies upright and trying to make them feel light.
• Ask the children to run across the area and every so often lift one heel to try and touch their bottoms. They should keep their knees bent and under their hips as they ground them.
• Tell the children to hop on one leg across the area and hop back on the other.

• Ask the children to run across the area with long strides, lifting their knees high.
• Let the children run around the area. Tell them to keep their heads steady and their toes pointing towards the finishing line. Also, see whether they can synchronise their arm swings with their leg movements.

Having worked on improving their own skills the children can join together for some class activities.

• Organise some shuttle run relays across 20m and then 30m and so on.
• Let the children play 'Circular passing rounders' (see page 119).

• Organise some team sprint relays over 2 × 25m using a baton. The first child in each team should run around a cone and return to the back of her line. She should give the baton to the last child in the team who passes it forwards to the child at the front of the line, who must then run around the cone and so on until the first child reaches the front of the line again.
• Ask the children to form teams of four and jog around the area. As soon as they are moving together, the child at the back of the line should sprint to the front. Immediately, the child now at the back should start to sprint to the front. This

should continue until the whole team have moved from the back to the front. This can become a competitive event by seeing which team completes the rotation of leader first over a fixed distance.
• Organise some individual races over 50m and 80m distances.

Jumping: standing broad jump

Remind the children about the correct technique for doing a standing broad jump (see page 63). Let the children practise jumping for a while and then move on to look at ways in which they can improve their performances.
• Ask the children to hop on one foot and then jump using both feet across 15m.
• Tell them to jump into the air as high as they can.
• Help the children to practise the five basic jumps (see page 92).
• Ask the children to rock backwards and forwards transferring their body weight from their toes to their heels. As they move on to their toes they should swing their arms forward and as they shift their weight to their heels they should swing their arms backwards.

The children should now practise making standing broad jumps again.

They should lean their bodies forwards and swing their arms forwards as they take-off, transferring their weight on to their toes. Once in the air they should continue leaning forwards and stretch their arms. They should lean forward as they land and bring the whole of their feet down forcefully.

The children should now be given the opportunity to take part in some enjoyable class activities in which they can improve their skills.
• Organise the children into teams of four. The children in each team should stand one behind the other and take turns to jump into and out of four hoops. The hoops should be laid out on the ground about 30cm apart and the children should use both feet together to jump. Once they have made all four jumps they should return to the end of the team.
• Ask the children to each face a partner and crouch down. Each pair should try to knock each other over by pushing each other with a flat hand against a flat hand.
• Tell the children to count how many times they can jump, keeping their feet together, into and out of a hoop in 20 seconds.
• If you are working indoors, put down several mats and ask the children to practise jumping with two feet together on to and across the mats. Ask them to do three successive jumps in order to warm up the ankle area and encourage ankle strength.
• Ask the children to work in pairs to measure how far they can jump. Record the measurement on a class record sheet or the child's own personal record sheet.

Throwing: overarm

Reteach the throwing technique which is explained on pages 48–49 and then set up various practices to encourage the children to throw for distance. Encourage the children to measure and record how far they throw each time.
• Present the children with several arm strengthening practices, such as bunny jumps, cat-springs, the caterpillar walk, press-ups and the seal walk.
• Ask the children to each throw a large ball to a partner across various distances.
• Tell the children to sit down and practise throwing large balls to their partners. They should use both hands and throw the balls from above their heads.

The children can then try a similar practice but from a kneeling or a standing position.
• Ask the children to throw large balls to their partners from their chests. First they should work from a sitting position and then progress to kneeling and standing. Once the children have practised this ask them to use a tennis-sized ball.

There are some additional points for overarm throwing technique which it would be worth teaching the children at this stage. The long distance throw is based on the principle of co-ordinating all the body movements so that the body momentum can be transferred into the throw. Therefore, the children could try to throw the ball at an angle of 45°. They should also use body rotation to transfer their weight from their back feet to their front feet.

The children could then incorporate these teaching points into the following class activities.
• Ask the children to throw their balls as far as they can and measure the throws.
• Organise a game of 'Danish rounders' (see page 129).
• Let the children play 'Circular passing rounders' (see page 119).
• Ask the children to play 'King ball' (see page 130).
• Ask the children to play 'Bombardment' (see page 120).

Running: 800m

It is *essential* that children do not attempt to run this distance until they have had experience of walking and jogging for 800m. This should be done over a number of lessons, spanning several weeks.

Below is an example of how this might be done:
• Week 1: walk briskly for 400m.
• Week 2: jog gently at first, then walk to complete 400m.
• Week 3: let the children walk, jog, walk according to their ability for up to 800m. Allow them to jog when they are ready.
• Week 4: repeat Week 3 and then ask the children to see how far they can jog before they have to stop and walk. Can they keep going for 800m?
• Week 5: children who can jog around the 400m distance without stopping can now be encouraged to jog for 800m.
• Week 6: encourage the children to run gently around the track without stopping. (Allow the children who need to, to slow down and jog and walk.)

Some children will not be capable of running 800m and should not be made to try. Nevertheless, all the children can be encouraged to walk for 800m.

The children could also take part in the following class activities to help build up their stamina for running 800m.
• Ask the children to line up one behind the other and walk for 400m. The child at the end of the line should immediately jog to the front of the line and continue to walk. As soon as this child starts walking again, the child now at the end of the line should jog to the front and so on until everyone has had a turn.
• Line up the children in several teams. Each team should walk 400m. The child at the end of each team should jog in and out of his team until he reaches the front of the line and then continue to walk. As soon as he starts to walk again, the child now at the end of the line should start to jog in and out of her team as before.
• Divide the children into four teams and ask each team to walk one behind the other until you call out 'jog', 'walk' or 'skip'. The children must keep the same formation, but change their movements.
• Create a jogging or walking trail around the school grounds, as shown in the following diagram. Design the trail with the children, deciding where to place a variety

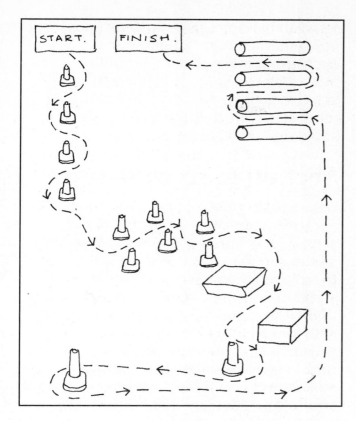

of obstacles such as cones or utilising obstacles already in the school grounds.

Hop, step and jump

The children will have already practised the fundamental aspects of hopping, stepping and jumping in the course of athletics, dance and gymnastics lessons during Key Stage 1. However, they will need to work on the following practices to improve their performances.
• Ask the children to hop across the area.
• Tell the children to stand with two feet together and swing their arms forwards and backwards. Tell them to flex their knees and jump on to one foot.
• Ask the children to hop on the spot.
• Ask the children to leap as far as they can from one of their feet to the other.
• The children should finally practise the whole movement. They should start off with both their feet together and hop on to one foot and then step on to the other and finally jump on to two feet.
• Encourage the children to play 'Hopscotch', to increase their awareness of the hop, step and jump technique.

Class activities

• Let the children practise walking for about 15m with long, stretched strides.
• Ask the children to hop on one of their legs, then on their other legs, then to skip, and finally to run as fast as possible across the same distance.
• Encourage the children to move freely around the area practising the hop, step and jump sequence of movements.
• If the ground surface is suitable the children should practise one or two arm strengthening activities such as the caterpillar walk (see page 18) or the clock face.

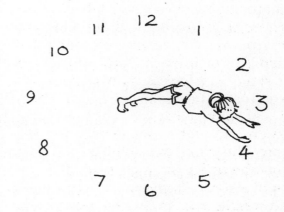

To perform the 'clock face' the children should keep their feet still and, in a stretched position, move their hands around in a circle in a clockwise direction.

Activity stations

Once the children have had an opportunity to work on and refine all their athletic skills, it is a good idea to set up activity stations where groups of children will be able to work on particular skills at the same time. In organising activity stations, the children should be arranged into groups of six and encouraged to set up their own activity and decide how they are going to measure the event. Each group should visit each activity during one lesson.

The examples which follow show two plans for setting up activity stations.

Plan one

• Station one: hop, skip and jump (land on a mat).
• Station two: throw a large ball overhead.
• Station three: timed runs over 50m.
• Station four: standing broad jump.
• Station five: individual shuttle runs between two markers placed 15m apart.

Plan two

• Station one: timed runs over 80m.
• Station two: hop, step and jump.
• Station three: throwing a small ball as far as possible.
• Station four: standing broad jump.
• Station five: timed 50m shuttle run relays.
Other ideas for activity stations might include:
• three jumps with both feet together (measure);
• hop on one leg across 15m (time);
• run (slalom-style) in and out of ten skittles placed 0.5m apart (time);
• run around four skittles placed 15m apart (time);
• run over three canes placed on tennis ball boxes or similar supports (time);
• walk up to and jump from a start line – jumping from one foot to land on two feet (measure);

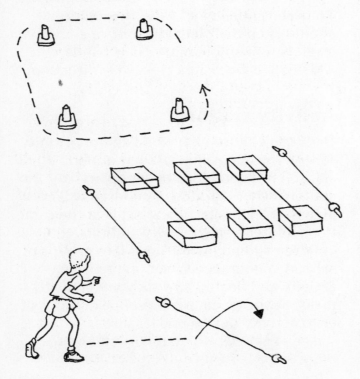

• run and jump from a start line (measure).
   Choose activity stations so that when each group moves from one station to the next, they change from an energetic activity, such as sprinting, to something more static, such as throwing or doing standing broad jumps.

Section four: cool-down

Before asking the class to assemble for cool-down activities at the end of the session, it is important to make sure that all the apparatus has been gathered ready to be taken indoors, or replaced in the store area. Ask the children to find a space of their own and try some of the following activities to bring the session to a satisfactory conclusion, while at the same time helping the children to 'unwind'.
• Ask the children to sit with their legs in a straddle position and hold their ankles and rock from side to side.
• Ask the children to balance on one leg.
• Tell them to stand still and close their eyes.
• Ask them to practise scissor jumps.
• Ask the children to walk behind a partner, following him wherever he goes.
• Tell the children to stand on tiptoe and count to ten.
• Try out a breathing exercise whereby the children raise their arms as they breathe in and lower them as they breathe out.
• Draw letters in the air backwards (that is, forwards from the children's point of view) and ask them to copy you to spell out the word 'athletics'.

Evaluation

To evaluate children's work in athletics, it is probably best to use a performance table which has been compiled by one of the organisations that promote athletics awards for primary school children, such as the Ten Step Award Scheme and the ESSA TSB Award Scheme. These tables are presented clearly and provide sets of graded performances which children of all abilities will be able to achieve.

Chapter 9
Dance

'Pupils should:
• **make dances with clear beginnings, middles and ends involving improvising, exploring, selecting and refining content, and sometimes incorporating work from other aspects of the curriculum, in particular music, art and drama;**
• **be given opportunities to increase the range and complexity of body actions, including step patterns and use of body parts.**
• **be guided to enrich their movements by varying shape, size, direction, level, speed, tension and continuity .**
• **in response to a range of stimuli, express feelings, moods and ideas and create simple characters and narratives in movement'** (Programme of Study).

Dance is an essential part of a balanced physical education programme. Although it is concerned with the development of the artistic and aesthetic side of our nature, it is inextricably linked with three very important physical factors:
• the acquisition and control of bodily movements;
• versatility in the use of the body;
• strength and flexibility.

The three principles of dance are composition, performance and appreciation and all three principles should be regarded as interrelated. When they are taught, therefore, they should all be taught together. Inevitably, the ability to compose a dance or dance sequence will depend on the age of the child, but even the youngest dancer can be encouraged to think of movements in response to the stimuli of either a piece of music, various sounds or words or to suggestions made in relation to a particular task. From such beginnings children can be encouraged to improvise and eventually to select suitable movements which they can then practise, refine and shape into a finished performance. From the start of the process to the finish, dance appreciation can be constantly encouraged, mainly by involving the children in observing and analysing all aspects of the developing performance, both their own and that of others. Helping children to acquire a knowledge of artistic criteria will undoubtedly lead them to a better understanding of the differences in style and form.

All Key Stage 2 teachers have a rich variety of dance forms to choose from when they come to select syllabus material for the dance curriculum. Again, the DES proposals (*PE for ages 5 to 16*, 1991) are helpful:
'Dance in its broad cultural context includes three interrelated categories:
• popular culture/art: dances of the time, for example, Bhangra, Jazz, Ballroom, Tap, Street Dancing, Ballet, Contemporary, South Asian forms, African People's dance, New Dance:
• traditional/folk: dances from different countries, for example, Morris, Clog, some Asian forms, some African People's Dance;
• historical: dances of the past, for example, *Farandole, Charleston, Minuet, Tango, Lindy Hop*'.

Clearly not all aspects of each dance category can be included in a four year syllabus, indeed most teachers will not have enough background knowledge to teach even some of the dance forms listed above. It is also true to say that up to now many teachers of older primary school children have not been required to teach dance on a regular basis and consequently may feel that they need a lot of support in establishing and teaching this aspect of the physical education curriculum.

Those teachers, however, who teach dance regularly undoubtedly find it both stimulating and rewarding. The best teaching not only develops children's movement experiences, but often does so through an exciting blend of dance, drama, art and music.

Wherever dance is taught well, it invariably means that an environment is created where both excitement and creative activity feed the imagination and the senses, often leading children to new experiences which are often denied them in other areas of the curriculum. Dance is a medium through which all children, including the disabled, can enjoy bodily exercise, bodily education and bodily expression more readily than in any other aspects of physical education.

Finally, it is important to remember how significant dance has become in the lives of young children – reason enough, it would seem, to actively pursue it in school. The pop culture, promoted through the media, may have a lot to answer for, but whichever way it is regarded, it ranks high in importance in many children's eyes. All teachers should recognise it as a very useful foundation on which to build a dance programme within the physical education curriculum. Disco dancing has also been shown to have health related benefits, associated with exercise performed at a high rate of intensity. In addition, dancing to contemporary music allows the children to express their emotions and feelings freely as they move to the mood, tempo and beat of the music. All children seem to have a kinaesthetic sense embedded in their bodies which dance experiences can awaken. Fortunately, unlike some other aspects of the physical education curriculum, this awakening does not have to wait for perfected bodily movements in order to manifest itself. Free expression can always be carefully nurtured and guided until dance forms emerge which have more clarity and more precision.

The material which follows in this chapter is primarily intended for non-specialists who might need a simplified series of lessons to help them formulate a programme for the first time. The material comes, however, with a note of caution, for it is extremely important for any teacher attempting dance to recognise that much will depend on his enthusiasm for the subject. As with most classroom activities, if the teacher is stirred then, most likely, the children will be stirred too. This is especially true in the use of stimuli for dance. A piece of music or a poem enthusiastically promoted and effectively used is often the starting point for interesting and creative work.

It is through 'starting points' and a consideration of various stimuli appropriate for dance that we now begin.

Stimuli for dance

There are eight main stimuli from which to access the subject matter for dance. These can be categorised as follows:
• music;
• percussion;
• voice sounds;
• language;
• literature;
• nature;
• artefacts;
• festivals/rituals;

Music

Junior-aged children usually respond well to rhythmic, lively music, particularly if the whole notion of dancing to music has already been introduced in the classroom. This will be more pronounced if it is the first occasion on which a lesson is based around dancing to music and especially if there is a new teacher in control. As the children become more confident they will almost certainly be able to respond to any music which produces a change of mood. There are many musical forms to help them at this stage, in fact the only type of music to avoid would be that commonly associated with the epic film. This particular variety is unsuitable because it is often so full of emotionally reactive stimuli that children find it hard to manage the many messages that are being conveyed. On the other hand, there are many other forms which are eminently suitable to use. Among these are the suite and divertimenti,

together with themes and variations; all highly appropriate, principally because they are short and easy to use. (A list of suitable music for dance is suggested at the end of the book.)

Percussion

Percussion sounds are usually very effective in stimulating children's movement. Initially, you can play the various instruments to accompany suggested movements, but eventually, the children themselves should be encouraged to select and play an instrument to accompany a group dance. This would be especially appropriate where the children may have 'composed' their own dances.

The drum is probably the most frequently used percussion instrument, mainly because it is the easiest to play and produces a short-lived sound which can be varied in pitch. Many children have been helped to perform their first dance sequences in response to the rhythmic sounds of a drum. On the other hand, gongs and cymbals with their resonant and

explosive sounds can be used to emphasise strong, direct, 'expansive' movements followed by soft, indirect movements. For other direct, strong, quick movements use castanets and rhythm sticks. Maracas, coupled with bells, can often encourage smooth, turning movements or small gestures and steps, while the triangle can be used to produce delicate, sustained movements. The most versatile of all the percussion instruments, however, is the tambourine. Its sound encourages a wide range of movement including gesture, contracting and expanding, travelling, stepping and jumping, and twisting and turning.

Voice sounds

It is important to recognise that children can control their voice sounds more readily than they can control percussion instruments. It would appear, then, that of all the stimuli suggested, the voice should be the most effective. However, although this is undoubtedly true, it is not always possible to use the voice as a stimulus, particularly if the atmosphere of the lesson or the children's mood is not right. Having said that, exciting, atmospheric – and sometimes humorous – movement sequences can be achieved with children working only with their voices as stimuli.

Language

The words of our language can often be used to help children to respond bodily. Before, for example, introducing them to the rhythm of poetry, the single word with its meaning and often onomatopoeic overtones is very effective in stimulating, accompanying and developing chosen movements. It is very difficult not to respond to the movement suggestions implicit in such words as, 'pop', 'explode', 'wither', 'slither', and 'punch'. Words such as 'slash', 'jab' and 'flick' can also be used to match meaning to sound-interpreted movement. Children should be encouraged to create sequences of words to develop into patterns which, when repeated, can form both dance patterns and rhythmical sequences such as 'snap, crackle, pop' or 'flutter, whirl, punch'.

Literature

The rhythms and beat of poetry give it a natural affinity to dance and where these two art forms merge satisfactorily, they can evoke and awaken in children deep aesthetic responses.

Stories often lend themselves to the creation of dance in a different way. Here the stimulus can be through theme, character or idea – most children, for example, enjoy robotic and mechanical themes, space themes and so on. Often, where children have shared a story and given some thought to its characters, their dance and dance-drama interpretations become very detailed. Traditional literature, such as the Bible or Shakespeare's works, is often a good source of stimulation when working with older junior children. (See Resources section for suitable poetry anthologies and books.)

Nature

Many dance sequences can be stimulated by the movements associated with insects, birds and animals and also from a close examination of the growth of plants and trees. Initially, such sequences can be created as simple interpretations of scientific observation in the classroom, for example, the life cycle of a butterfly. However, these can be developed into more complex dance-dramas in which, for example, the movements of an insect are combined with those of a bird.

You can deepen responses of this kind by helping the children to find different 'characteristics' of the creatures involved and suggesting distinctive and dynamic vocabulary associated with them; for example, a cat could be described as prowling, scanning, pouncing, clawing, stalking and so on.

Often, dance sequences and dance-dramas can be created after studying such natural phenomena as water, fire, volcanoes, earthquakes and so on. Topics like these will generate word associations which are fun for children to collect and exciting to use as accompaniment to their dances.

Artefacts

Interesting artefacts or props can be used to stimulate dance. They are a particularly useful aid for mentally-handicapped children, who often find confidence and security when holding a ribbon, scarf or piece of material as they dance. In fact, all children can benefit from dancing with such artefacts. Objects such as a chiffon scarf can be waved in the air while the children watch and then copy the movement or perform with it. In the main, artefacts can be used to both heighten dance action and also lend extra meaning to it. For example, the circle can represent a moon, a wheel, endlessness and so on.

Festivals and rituals

Most children enjoy celebrating festivals such as Christmas, Easter and Diwali and are usually happy to explore, during school time, the dynamic actions associated with them. Often, worship and music are part of the fabric of such celebrations. Where music occurs, there is an obvious means to explore movement patterns. Worship can be incorporated into dances of praise or sorrow, where actions of bowing, kneeling, hand gestures and so on, can all be combined and developed to give symmetrical form, rhythmic pattern and a gathering dynamism to the total experience.

The music of other countries and cultures will also add immeasurably to the expressive nature of creative dance movements. The geographical dimension, initiated in the classroom, may stimulate interest in such diverse cultures as those of the North American Indians, Aztecs, Native Australians (Aborigines) and the Balinese, all of whom possess rituals which include a high proportion of story-dance elements.

Section one: developing dance skills

This section is concerned with developing basic dance skills, together with movement and dance experiences, into real dance situations which could be linked to cross-curricular themes. It is set out as a series of lessons and the 'philosophy' of each lesson is developed from a basic framework:
• what we move: travelling actions; actions on the spot;
• where we move: movement directions (forward, backwards, sideways); pathways (straight, curved, zigzag, circle); levels (high, medium, low);
• how we move: speed of movement (quick, slow, sudden, smooth); quality of movement (heavy/light, strong/soft);
• who we move with: alone; a partner; threes; group (cluster, line, circle).

It is recommended that each lesson should have the following structure.
• Warm-up: an initial activity to both create the atmosphere for the lesson and prepare the body for dance activity.
• Movement training: a balance should be maintained between locomotor (travelling) movements and body movements performed on the spot, energetic and calm movements, and individual, partner and group work.
• Dance: the climax of the lesson should be the creation, by the children, of a dance, dance sequence or dance-drama which may take one week or several weeks to perfect.
• Cool-down: an activity should be chosen which has a calming effect on the class.

The dance ideas presented at the end of each lesson are offered in developmental order, for example, the first dance idea is more suitable for Year 3 while the fourth dance idea is more suitable for Year 6.

Lesson one: body awareness

Use a percussion instrument, such as a tambourine, to stimulate movement.

Warm-up

Tap the tambourine, keeping a steady beat, and encourage the children to walk, step, jump and run to the sound.

You can then shake the tambourine and ask the children to shake their arms, fingers, feet, legs and their whole bodies.

Movement training

Tap the tambourine to produce short, staccato sounds and ask the children to:
• poke their index fingers, then thumbs and then their fists into the space around them;
• push the back of each hand away from their bodies bodies at different levels;
• tap their heels with their hand (behind themselves);
• kick into the space around them;
• bend to tap their elbows against their heels and then their big toes;
• walk around the area on tiptoe;
• tap the floor with their heels and then their big toes.

Use your finger nails to make circular movements across the surface of the tambourine, then stop, wait for three seconds and repeat the sound. Ask the children to:
• move their palms away from each other and towards each other at different levels and taking different pathways;
• use the little finger side of each hand to make pathways in the air at different levels;
• use one elbow to trace patterns in the air.

Dance one

Ask the children to work with a partner to create a dance based on the movements they practised earlier in the lesson.
• At what level are they going to start their dances?

• Where will they position themselves in relation to their partners?
• Are they going to plan the levels at which they are going to dance?
• Will they work in opposition to their partners or together?
• Which parts of their bodies will they use?
• How will their dances finish?

Encourage the children further by creating a percussion rhythm based on the sounds they responded to earlier.

Dance two

Ask the children to create a dance based on having a conversation with their partners – using hand gestures to relay meaning.

Dance three

Ask the children to create a dance where they keep the palms of their hands touching their partners' palms.

Dance four

The children could create, with a partner, a meeting and parting dance using their knees and elbows only. Each pair could agree to meet at certain points in their dance to touch elbows or knees and then move apart again.

Alternatively, they could move from one touched position to another.

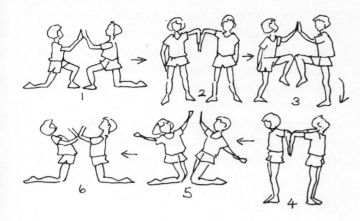

Cool-down

Ask the children to stand up straight, keeping good body tension. They should then relax into a slumped position, but while still remaining standing. Tell them to stretch into any body shape, hold it and return to a normal standing position.

Lesson two: awareness of weight and time

Use various percussion instruments such as tambourines, drums, castanets, bells, maracas, chime bars and so on, as stimuli for movements.

Warm-up

Make different sounds, beats and rhythms with the instruments and ask the children to move about the area in response.

Movement training

• Use a cymbal and let the children practice making strong thrusting and slashing movements with their arms followed by smooth, gliding movements which become slower and slower.
• Use castanets and guide the children so that they make sudden, direct, strong movements with their fists, elbows, hips and finally their shoulders.
• Use bells to inspire a range of slow, soft indirect, movements, followed by a variety of short, soft steps around the room.

• Use chime bars, played softly, to encourage the children to make a range of delicate, light movements using only slight muscle tension. They should be guided to use their fingers, hands, wrists and arms, and then their heads and upper bodies.

Dance one

The children can work in small groups and choose one percussion instrument with which to work. One child should play the instrument, while the others create a dance. The dance need not be structured, but should have a clear starting and finishing shape. As they work ask them if their movements are strong or light.

Dance two

Let the children work in small groups. One child in each group can play an instrument and wherever he goes, the rest of the group must follow. He can vary the rhythm so that they move high and low, and quickly and slowly.

Dance three

The children should work in small groups with one child in each group playing a percussion instrument. The children should initially form a group shape. The instrument should then be played near one child, who should respond by moving to another place. Each child is then rearranged in a similar manner to develop a new group shape.

Dance four

Tell the children to work in groups of five or seven and create their own meeting and parting dances. They can choose which percussion instruments to use to accompany their dances.
• How will they start?
• Will they have different parts of their bodies and at different levels?
• Will they need to vary the speed of their movements?

- Could the group split, so that two meet in one place and three in another?
- What about three meeting two or four meeting one?
- What kind of movements do they need to incorporate? Will they use strong, light, sustained or sudden movements or will they use a variety?
- Can they incorporate moments of stillness and silence?
- How will they end the dance?

Cool-down

Ask the children to curl up, but be ready to stretch out again slowly, using any body shape they choose. While the children do this exercise, gently play the chime bars. They should hold their body shapes still, without making a sound, until you start to play the chime bars again and then they should start to return to their curled up position.

Lesson three: locomotion and location in space

In this lesson the stimuli for dance and movement are words.

Warm-up

Call out various action words and ask the children to respond in the way that the words suggest, for example:
- shake, shake, shake all over…;
- step, step, step, jump, jump, jump…;
- punch, punch, punch, kick, kick, kick…;
- step, step and turn, turn, turn….

Movement training

Sit with the children in a circle. Each child should say his name three times and touch the next child who says her name three times and so on. Once everyone has had a turn, the first child should say his name three times and continue to repeat his name after touching the next child. Prearrange with the children that when you

lift your hands upwards you want more sound and when you move them downwards you want less sound.

Carry on working in this way, but this time, each child can choose an arm movement to make instead of saying her name. Each child should join in with his own movement until the whole class is moving together.

Dance one

Ask the children to work together and make up a repetitive sequence from the following words: 'press, gather, scatter, rise, fall, slither, zigzag, straight, curl, stretch, twist, turn and hold'.

Dance two

Ask the children to form groups of three and make up a repetitive dance pattern based on a catchy jingle such as 'snap, crackle and pop'.

Dance three

The children can work with a partner and, starting in a back to back position, make up a movement sequence based on the following instructions:
- twist away, rise up and sink down, reach up high and jump to face your partner;
- one person rise and one person sink in turn, three times, and hold the finished position.

Dance four

For this dance the children can choose their own group size and words. Encourage them to mix jingles with single words, for example: 'Tip, tap, tip, tap – boom!

The following are groups of useful words which suggest movements:
- elegant, proud, stately;
- rip, flap, sever, screw, scoop, sweep;
- swing, sink, sweep, settle, spread;
- linger, mingle, tingle;
- sting, stab, slash, poke;
- stretch, shrink, snatch, perish;

• prick, poke, pierce, push, pace;
• waver, wander, flutter, soar, flap;
• dominate, dispute, abolish, impose, power, crisis, destruction, collapse, conflict, revolution;
• surrender, disperse;
• attack, defend, victory, defeat, vanquished;
• simmer, stutter, sparkle, soar, dissolve, smoulder, fusion, erupt, bulge;
• peace, tranquillity, silence, windless;
• mutter, chunter, chatter, transmit;
• crooked, wicked, wild, violent, danger.

Cool-down

Ask the children to move their fingers into different shapes at different levels as you say quietly, 'Stretch and hold, stretch and hold…'.

Lesson four: matching movements to word patterns

This lesson uses poetry and jingles as the stimuli for the movement.

Warm-up

The children can do the actions and movements suggested in the following rhymes. Year 3 and 4 children could use the rhyme 'Teddy bear, teddy bear, turn around'. However, Year 5 and 6 children could try the following:

Cowboy Joe from Mexico
Hands up, stick 'em up
Drop your guns
And pick 'em up.

The children can then gallop about the room to the rhyme:

Galloping, galloping up the lane
Galloping, galloping down again.
Galloping, galloping night and day
Galloping, galloping away! Away!

Finally, change the rhyme and let the children do the actions to the following:

Shake hands with your partner. (*Shake right hands.*)
Shake hands with your partner. (*Shake left hands.*)
Shake hands with your partner. (*Shake both hands.*)
As you have done before. (*Shake both hands.*)

Movement training

When using extracts from poetry as the basis for movement it is a good idea to read the whole poem to the children before they start to move to it. After the poem has been read, the children should be encouraged to move appropriately until they achieve a sustained, flowing movement. As they work, repeat the poem, helping the children to feel the mood and essence of the words, perhaps stopping after particular phrases so that the children can sense the scene.

Couplets, single lines or whole stanzas taken from poems can be used to help children as they begin to respond through movement and dance to poetic language; for example:
• 'icy sting' (from 'Sky in the pie' by Roger McGough in his anthology of the same name);
• 'electrical tingles from hit after hit' (from 'The hallow men' by T.S. Eliot);
• 'gesture without motion', 'I'm moving along slowly along to your place', 'Then the green grass sprouted' (from 'The creation – a Negro sermon' by J.W. Johnson in *God's Trombones*);
• 'I like to slide my bulk
Against the nylon ankles of young ladies' (from 'The cat' by Gareth Owen in his anthology, *Song of the City*).

When sharing poems which might awaken strong emotions, let the children explore the movement sequences which they think best illustrate their feelings towards the poetry. It is particularly important that this sort of work is seen as a whole class activity with the children showing each other how they have responded to poetry in the movements they produce.

Dance ideas

Teachers will already be using poetry as part of their work in the classroom and many of these poems will be suitable for dance lessons. The following three suggestions can be used as starting points for imaginative and creative dance. They are not offered in any particular order nor necessarily are they for different age groups, but are simply examples of how poetry can be used to stimulate dance.

Humorous verse

Children often enjoy moving to humorous verse and there are several poems which can be used as the basis for whole dance or movement pieces. A particular example with good movement possibilities is, 'People I'd rather not talk about' by Roger McGough in his book *Sky in the Pie: a book of new poems*.

Anthologies

Almost every collection of poems that is suitable for older primary children will contain some poems centred around the seasons. The *Autumn Book* by James Reeves, for example, is a rich source of poems and rhymes which can be used to stimulate movement. Many of the Puffin collections have suitable poems too. Try also *Sky in the pie* by Roger McGough or

'Stopping by woods on a snowy evening' by Robert Frost in *Illustrated Poets Series: Robert Frost*. Another excellent poem associated with weather and the seasons which can be spoken aloud while the children move and use percussion in a dramatic fashion is 'Man the Musicmaker' by Roger McGough, also in *Sky in the Pie*.

Fire and fireworks are topics which open up many movement possibilities for the children. It will not be very difficult to stimulate their imaginations when nearing Bonfire Night. There are several poems which can be used, for example, 'November the Fifth' by Leonard Clark in the *Young Puffin Book of Verse* and 'Fireworks' by James Reeves in his *Autumn Book*.

Children will enjoy practising firework movements. They can crouch low, suddenly shooting up high for rockets; stand with their wrists crossed in front of their stomachs and vigorously circle both arms together for Catherine wheels; jump all over the area on both feet in short, sharp movements for fire crackers; quickly wiggle their fingers for sparkles and so on.

Religious poems

Religious poems or extracts taken from religious texts can often form the basis for extremely thoughtful movement. One of my favourites is 'The creation – a Negro sermon' by James Weldon Johnson in *God's Trombones*. Religious texts vary of course, but it would certainly be possible for the children to combine their work on the text with an appreciation of religious art works, especially since many famous pictures show people at prayer. These prayer positions can be linked with other movements to produce effective sequences.

Cool-down

Short extracts from poems or short poems in their entirety can be used to end lessons. Many poems have the added advantage of being rather soothing in their total effect thus bringing movement and dance to a satisfying conclusion.

Lesson five: matching movements to sounds

Use voice and body sounds as the stimuli for movement in this lesson.

Warm-up

Ask the children to walk around the room in silence until you use your voice or body to make a sound, for example, 'clicking' your tongue or snapping your fingers. When the children hear the sound they should make a short, quick, direct movement with their fingers and hands. You can repeat this several times making different sounds each time.

You could also try a variation whereby the children move their bodies or hop on one foot to the sound. You could also try making different facial expressions, changing from a happy face to a sad face to an angry face to a horrible face and asking the children to copy you.

Movement training

Use your voice to make a 'Whee...' sound starting low and quietly and building up to a crescendo. The children should curl up on the floor and listen as you make the sound. As the sound changes the children should rise up until they are stretched up as far as possible. Make the same sound again, but this time starting loudly and finishing low and tell the children to gradually curl up.

The children can then make their own voice sounds to accompany their movements as they stretch and curl into different shapes. If they make a loud sound, they should be encouraged to make strong, positive movements leading to a strong static shape where all the muscles are tensed, with their fists clenched and feet gripping the floor. By contrast, a soft, quiet sound should produce gentle, indirect movements.

Try making a 'creaking' sound and tell the children to raise and lower their shoulders in response or you could make a 'tutting' sound with your tongue. The children can nod their heads from side to side, as they hear the sound, and bend their arms so that their palms face upwards and move from side to side. They can also move their hips and knees from side to side.

Try whistling and ask the children to make circular and curving movements in the space around their bodies and at all levels. They can use different parts of their bodies to lead the movement. Ask the children to try and whistle and, at the same time, make circular and curving patterns on the floor with one foot.

Clap your hands and tell the children to step forwards diagonally on each clap or they could punch the air with their fists.

Dance one

Ask the children to find partners. One child can make a sound while her partner moves to it. Once they have created a sequence the children can change roles.

Dance two

Ask the children to work with partners to create movement patterns. They should pick three different sounds such as clicking fingers, clapping hands and whistling and dance as they make the sounds. When they have decided what they are going to do, ask them to think about the levels at which they will be working, deciding how they will start and finish. Can each pair repeat their pattern three times?

Dance three

Tell the children to work in groups of four and make up dances using as many voice and body sounds as they like to accompany their movements. Ask them to think about the following questions.
• What level are they going to start at?
• In what position?
• Which parts of their bodies are they going to move?

- Where are they going to move to?
- What speed will they move at?
- How much strength (weight) will they use?

Dance four

Working in groups of four ask the children to compose dances using voice and body sounds. They can choose one sound and work together or they could use contrasting sounds at the same time. Tell them to vary the sounds they use and the speed of their movements. Finally, they should think about the overall shape of their composition, for instance, whether the movements and group formations they have chosen form interesting patterns for spectators. They should check that their composition has:
- interesting starting and finishing shapes;
- contrasting group shapes;
- clearly defined movement patterns;
- changes of speed and times of stillness.

Cool-down

Face the class and make a series of movements. Ask the children to copy you in silence.

Hum loudly and ask the children to gyrate their arms and bodies as you hum. Gradually, the children should move more softly and slowly, to the constant sound.

Lesson six: matching movements to recorded music

This lesson is constructed around the tape of the *BBC Sporting themes* which is obtainable from most record shops (see Resources). It has been chosen to illustrate how any commercially available recording can form the stimulus for dance.

Warm-up

Play the theme music from *Grandstand* and

ask the children to jog on the spot. They can then start to jump sideways from right to left and left to right as they jog. Ask the children to alternate jogging on the spot with jogging and jumping sideways, performing eight of each in turn.

Move on by telling the children to do deep knee bends and then to extend both arms and bend both arms together, first in front of their bodies and then to each side. They can then combine bending their knees with bending their arms.

Movement training

Play the theme tune for the *Test cricket* and ask the children to clench their fists loosely and extend their index fingers. They must then stretch their arms, so that their index fingers lead their arms on different pathways around their bodies.

Let the children create their own movement patterns, choosing when to use both arms together and when to use each arm in turn. Their movements will have to be direct, strong and quick if they want to keep up with the music!

Play the theme for *World Cup Grandstand*. After the introduction to this track, the music becomes quick and rhythmical. Therefore, the children will need to listen to the whole track before they start to move to it. When the music is played again they can jump on the spot and jump and turn on the spot. They can then be encouraged to move about the room.

Play the signature tune for *Ski Sunday* and let the children listen to the music. They can then practise pivoting their feet on the spot, keeping their toes and knees together, and then moving so that their heels are together, but their knees apart. Ask the children to choose whirling, turning and spinning actions and move to the music, or suggest that they practise long steps, short steps, skipping steps, jumping steps and hopping steps anywhere in the room.

Dance one

Ask the children to work in groups of five

or six. Play the music for *Rugby Special* and tell the children to sit in a circle and together make up a rhythmical foot tapping dance which can be repeated three times.

Dance two

Ask the children to choose a partner and make up dances to the theme of the *Commonwealth Games*. Tell the children to face their partners and one child in each pair should make up a dance to the music based on extending and contracting movements. The other child in each pair should copy the movements.

Dance three

Let the children work in groups of six to make up a repetitive dance sequence to the *Darts* theme music. The dances should be based on nodding heads, punching with the arms, arm swinging movements and stamping actions with the feet. All the actions should be short, strong and direct. The children can choose their own group formation, for example, three standing behind three, six in a line side by side, or six in a line one behind the other.

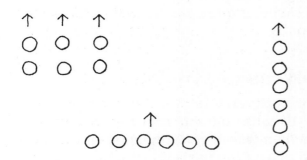

Dance four

Working in groups of three or five, ask the children to create a dance to the *World Cup Rugby* theme. They should base the dance on foot patterns, for example:
• jump from two feet to two feet when standing and when in a crouched position;
• walking, stepping, shuffling; one foot following the other; small steps in a high and a low body position;

• toe and heel tapping to a rhythm;
• movements on the spot, movement forwards, turning and twisting.

Cool-down

Ask the children to work in pairs, and lead them through a meeting and parting routine with their hands. A piece of music which suggests a peaceful mood such as 'Clair de lune' (Debussy) would be a suitable accompaniment.

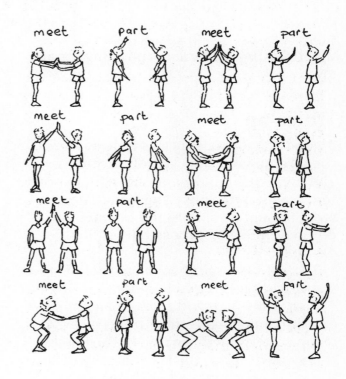

Lesson seven: movement responses to literature

This lesson is based around the book *The Lion, the Witch and the Wardrobe* by C.S. Lewis. Obviously, it will be important for the children to know and develop some feeling about the text, the story and the characters before this lesson, to inform their movement responses and improve the quality of their work.

There are many other books and stories which can be used in the same way, for example, *The Iron Man* by Ted Hughes can be used to particularly good effect, opening

up opportunities for incorporating art and craft work.

Warm-up

A good way of starting this type of work is to make up your own 'action' stories and and invite the children to move in response to the action the story suggests. The action story should be simple and contain lots of different movement possibilities, for example:

> The soldiers marched smartly along the dirt track leading to the jungle, swinging their arms high and straight and making a rhythmical pattern with their feet. As the undergrowth leading to the jungle became thicker, the track narrowed into a pathway and they had to march two by two, speeding up to a jogging trot. Suddenly, there was a short, sharp sound. They froze in their tracks. After a few seconds, they continued their journey, but now with long, slow, stealthy steps, turning their heads this way and that as they moved forward. The jungle became more and more overgrown with creepers and branches forcing them to slash their way through. They swung their arms high to break overhanging branches and brushed aside prickly, barbed bushes as they pushed onwards, ever onwards. The ground under their feet slowly began to get muddy and gradually they found themselves in a squashy, oozing wet bog through which they could hardly move except with the most tremendous effort....

or:

> It was a warm sunny day. All the children were happy as they skipped over the grass. Every so often, they bent down to pick the flowers which seemed to grow everywhere. They continued to skip and run and jump until they had to stop because they were so breathless. They took enormous deep breaths to recover, in and out, in and out, in and out. They stretched up their arms high, high towards the blue, cloudless sky and reached for the pleasant warmth of the sun....

Movement training

This part of the lesson concentrates specifically on the text of *The Lion, the Witch and the Wardrobe,* using character and plot as the basis for movement training.

The Queen of Narnia

Begin by building up a character profile of the Queen, often referred to as the Witch, by asking the children to tell you what the story tells us about her. References from the text which help to establish her identity might include:

• 'a slow cruel smile came across the Witch's face...' (Chapter 9);

• 'her eyes flaming...' (Chapter 4);

- 'speak vermin....' (Chapter 11);
- 'she's a horrible witch....' (Chapter 6);
- 'she has made an enchantment over the whole country...' (Chapter 6);
- 'taller than any woman that Edmund had ever seen...' (Chapter 3);
- 'proud and cold and stern...' (Chapter 3);
- 'savage smile, almost a sneer...' (Chapter 15).

You can then suggest the following movement possibilities to 'represent' the Queen.
- 'Practise strutting around the room with a straight back and smooth steps. Keep your chin high and make a cruel face.'
- 'Stand still and sweep each arm around several times to cast a magic spell.'
- 'Practise deep, swinging movements with your arms and swirl around and around at different levels as you cast your spell.'
- 'Practise making your fingers spikey and move them around your body with wide, gesturing movements of your arms.'

The Land of Narnia

Ask the children to tell you what Narnia was like when the Queen had cast her enchantment over it. Use the text to help provide illustrations, for example in Chapter 9 there is a description of all the animals and trees which the Queen had turned to stone, or:
- 'Above the dam there was what ought to have been a deep pool but now of course, a level floor of dark, green ice...' (Chapter 7);
- 'Where the water had been trickling and spurting through the dam there was now a glittering wall of icicles...' (Chapter 7).

The following suggestions for movement would complement these descriptions.
- The children can swirl and whirl all over the room at different levels and when you wave your 'wand' and say, 'Enchanted!' they must 'turn to stone' and stand still.
- Tell the children to make themselves into a sharp, spikey ice shape and then change into another sharp, spikey ice shape.
- Read the passage where Edmund left the Beaver's house and went out into the snow. (Chapter 9). Ask the children to pretend to be Edmund, slipping into deep drifts of snow, skidding on frozen puddles and tripping over fallen tree trunks in the dark.

The Lion

Build up a movement character for the Lion, Aslan, by using the descriptions of him in the story. Ask the children to suggest descriptive stanzas which they have read in the text, for example:
- 'terrible paws...' (Chapter 12);
- 'and as he opened his mouth to roar his face became so terrible...' (Chapter 15);
- 'he shot off faster than any horse can go...' (Chapter 15);
- limbs quivering, lashing... tail...' (Chapter 15).

You might then suggest that the children do the following 'lion' movements.
- Tell them to walk around on their hands and feet and show you their great, velvety paws.
- Ask them to crouch down, lift their heads, open their mouths and roar!
- Let them roll over and over on the floor and back on to all fours.
- Read the extract from Chapter 15 describing how a lion runs, silently and skilfully. Ask half of the class to stand still and pretend to be trees or lie down and pretend to be bushes while the rest of the children move in and out of the obstacles like the Lion. When appropriate the children can change over so that everyone has a chance to be a lion.

The statues

Read to the children the first two pages from Chapter 16. Then, encourage them to melt from a stone character into life, as you read the description beginning, 'For a second after Aslan had breathed on him, the stone lion...'.

Dance one

This is a whole class dance where one child has to pretend to be the Queen of Narnia, casting her magic spell on the class. She should whirl around the rest of the class turning them to stone as she whirls by them. Another child must be Aslan the

Lion, who prowls around breathing on the statues until all the class have melted and are 'living' again.

Dance two

Working in pairs, one child in each pair must be the Queen and the other can choose to be either an animal, a dwarf, a lion, or a giant. As the children pretend to be their character the Queen freezes each part of the body of her partner and then whirls around him.

Dance three

Ask the children to work in threes and make up a movement sequence called 'The icicles', based on the description in Chapter 7.

Dance four

Work with the children to make a dance-drama based on the end of Chapter 16, starting from: 'and all the rest of Aslan's army fighting desperately against the crowd of horrible creatures...'.

You can play background music to heighten the effect, for example, 'Mars' from *The Planets* Suite by Gustav Holst or 'Adagio for Strings' by Samuel Barber.

Cool-down

Ask the children to walk silently around the room making as little noise as possible. Meanwhile, read one or other of the following extracts from the story:
• 'Everything was perfectly still, as if he were the only living creature in that country. There was not even a robin or a squirrel among the trees, and the wood stretched as far as he could see. He shivered...' (Chapter 3);
• 'So they lived in great joy and if they ever remembered their life in this world it was only as one remembers a dream...' (Chapter 17).

Lesson eight: dances stimulated by artefacts

The stimuli for movement in this lesson comes from various artefacts such as handkerchiefs, scarves, hoops, balls, ropes, chairs and so on.

Warm-up

Tell each child to place a rope along the floor and then take a long, lunging step across it. The children should hold their positions and then slowly stretch out their arms as far as possible and hold the position again. Finally, they should slowly return to a standing position. They can repeat this movement, but this time zigzag across the length of the rope, leading with each leg alternately.

Movement training

Play the theme music from *Chariots of Fire* by Vangelis.
• Tell the children to hold handkerchiefs by one corner and, using wrist movements, move them up and down, from left to right and in circles on short pathways through the air. They can take the handkerchiefs high above their heads and low near to the ground.

• Show the children how to hold two corners of their handkerchiefs and hold them in front of their faces so that they cover them but do not touch them. Encourage the children to practise peeping over their handkerchiefs and from under them.

• Tell the children to move their handkerchiefs from place to place in every space around their bodies: high, low, to the right, to the left, and on straight, diagonal and circular pathways.

• Can the children wave 'goodbye' with their handkerchiefs? Ask to try to look sad and then look happy.

• Finally, ask the children to pretend to use their handkerchiefs to wipe away tears and then enlarge the movement by making large, circular movements with their wrists.

Dance one

Ask each child to choose and then walk in unison with a partner and, using a handkerchief, make up a dance based on the activities they did earlier in the lesson. They can select their choice of movements after listening to music such as 'Just be good to me' (Harris III/Lewis) from *Rapping with the Ladies*, recorded by Shabba Ranks.

Dance two

Ask the children to form groups of four or five and give each child a handkerchief. Let them listen to 'Crises' by Mike Oldfield, and then ask them to create a dance in which they move their handkerchiefs on different pathways and levels around their bodies.

Dance three

Ask the children to use their handkerchiefs to help them create a sad dance. They can choose the size of the group in which they work. Having worked on their dances for a short while let them listen to the music 'Aase's death' from *Peer Gynt* Suite No.1, Op.46 (Grieg) and then talk with them about which of the routines they have practised best express sadness.

Dance four

Choose a piece of music like Sinding's 'Rustle of Spring' and ask the children to create a handkerchief dance called 'Fluttering and dancing in the breeze'.

Lesson nine: dances concerned with festivals and rituals

This lesson uses the feelings of children as they respond to particular situations where music and the notion of festivals and/or ritual is important in the setting for the dance experience.

Warm-up

The following warm-up exercises can be accompanied by the music from *Joseph and the Amazing Technicolour Dreamcoat*.

• Ask the children to stand with a good posture and place their feet evenly and lift and lower their heels to the rhythm of the music. Tell them to place their feet in various positions while they lift and lower their heels.

• Ask the children to lift and lower their shoulders and elbows to the music.

• Tell the children to use different parts of their body to move to the rhythm of the music.

Movement training

• Ask the children to kneel down and press their hands together in a praying position. They should then gently and smoothly move their hands, keeping them together, as high as possible and then return them to their original position.

• Starting from a kneeling praying position, tell the children to describe circles in front of their bodies which go upwards and then outwards immediately in front of them, then high to the right and to the left.

• Let the children stand up and repeat all these movements. Their heads should be bowed at the start and finish of each circle, and their eyes should follow the action of their hands throughout each sequence. Then ask them to keep one of their hands in the praying position and let their other hands and arms move sideways (fingers pointing upwards, elbow bent) and back again.

• Encourage them to practise moving smoothly from a kneeling position to a standing position and from standing to kneeling.

Dance one

Play a recording of *Requiem* (Verdi) or some other similar 'sad' music. Make sure that the children become familiar with the sound and mood. Talk to them about the types of steps and pathways which they think would be appropriate for a 'sad' dance. This dance might also be a proud celebration of the lives of dead people. How do the children think this emphasis will change their movements?

Dance two

Play 'Air on a G string' (Bach) and show the children pictures of religious paintings in which the characters have assumed different 'prayer' positions. Ask the children to form groups of five and arrange themselves in a tableau which depicts 'prayer'. They can then work out a sequence of prayer movements where they either move all together or sometimes have only one or two people moving.

Dance three

Many religious festivals and ceremonies use processions. Play Handel's 'Arrival of the Queen of Sheba' and show the children how to walk smoothly, with their heads erect and their spines straight. Let them practise processing in a line so that they keep in time with the music and with each other. When they reach the end of the room, the first child should move to the right, and walk around the outside of the

room, and the second child should walk to the left and so on, until they all return to the starting position. The first and second child can then join hands and become a couple, as do the third and fourth and so on. They should then process down the length of the room and 'peel off' in couples again, returning to their starting positions. Each couple then joins another couple to form a 'four'. They can then process in lines of four and so on until all the children are processing around the room in a circle!

Dance four

Beat an 'African' style rhythm on a drum or use some appropriate music with an African beat, for example 'Graceland' by Paul Simon. Let the children practise moving around the room to the rhythm and encourage them to stamp hard on the ground to emphasise the beat of the drum. Remind them to move their upper bodies and arms as well.

The children can then make up their own dances to the rhythm. What sort of dance do they think would be appropriate to such a strong rhythm? Perhaps they might create a dance to celebrate a successful battle or harvest? If so, what kind of dance steps would they use and what kind of group formation would be appropriate? How could they make them 'happy' dances?

Lesson ten: dances stimulated by nature

This lesson is based on the study of mini-beasts, which is a popular area for investigation in the primary classroom. However, before any dance work is attempted, let the children study mini-beasts themselves. In this way, they will get to know some of the fundamental information about these creatures, in particular the way they move, before they start to consider how this information can be interpreted through dance.

Once the initial investigations are over,

the children can classify mini-beasts according to their methods of movement for example:
• those that walk and run: centipedes, millipedes, beetles, spiders, ants;
• those that fly: butterflies, bees, dragonflies, houseflies;
• those that jump and hop: grasshoppers, crickets, springtails, fleas;
• those that creep and slide: snails, slugs, worms, caterpillars.

Warm-up

Play 'The naming of cats' from *CATS* by Andrew Lloyd Webber and ask the children to walk to the music, lifting their heels and knees high. Tell them to make a chassé (slip-step) to the left and right and clap their hands. They can then make up their own step sequences in time to the music.

Movement training

Let the children practise moving like each of the mini-beast groups.

Walking and running

Tell the children to run quickly on tiptoe, pushing the balls of their feet firmly into the ground and taking small steps like beetles, ants or centipedes.

Ask them to stretch out and put their hands and feet on to the floor and move quietly, smoothly and slowly like a spider. They should keep their knees and elbows bent and occasionally stop and reach up on their toes and finger tips, with their elbows and knees turned out, to show a spider-shaped balance. Can they move backwards and sideways while keeping the spider shape? Did the spiders, beetles, ants or centipedes which they studied move in any other way?

Flying

Discuss with the children how insects fly and ask them to practise flying movements with their arms. Encourage them to think about the quality of their movements – whether insect wings beat strongly or

lightly, move forwards and backwards, up and down or quickly or slowly?

Jumping and hopping

Let the children practise jumping like grasshoppers and springtails. They should put their arms into a bent position with their elbows on their chests and the backs of their hands facing the direction in which they are travelling. They should then crouch down and leap upwards and forwards, returning to a crouching position.

Ask the children to put their feet together and stand up, keeping their arms in the same position and make big, bouncing jumps in different directions and then little, light jumps.

Creeping and sliding

Let the children choose whether they will try to move like a slug or a worm or a caterpillar. Remind them of the 'Caterpillar walk', described on page 18.

Dance one

Discuss with the children which of the movements they practised might be suitable for a dance based on the activities of bees, for example pollen collecting, swarming and describing flight paths.

Play 'Flight of the Bumble Bee' by Rimsky-Korsakov and let the children practise moving freely to the music. The children can then work in groups to decide what kind of dance they would like to create. You should move around the groups to give some ideas about starting shapes and give an opinion on the movements which the children are suggesting.

Dance two

Play the first part of *Danse Macabre* (Saint-Saëns) and let the children move freely to the music. Encourage them to imagine that caterpillars can dance and suggest that the children make up a caterpillar dance. Tell the children to kneel down and raise the front 'segments' of their bodies and sway

163

from side to side in time to the music, making circular movements with their heads.

Dance three

Play 'The Grasshopper's Dance' from the tape *Hello Children Everywhere (Volume 1)*. Suggest that the children walk, hop and jump to the music while keeping their upper bodies and arms in a grasshopper-like shape. Ask them to make up a repeating sequence which includes hopping or jumping and jogging actions. They can then use this sequence to create a 'barn dance' for eight pairs of grasshoppers.

Section two: country dance

This section is concerned with acquiring the dance skills which are necessary to perform traditional folk dancing.

Children aged eight to eleven are much more interested in dancing today than was perhaps the case even ten years ago. One of the reasons for this would seem to be the result of the media promotion of a 'teeny-bopper' culture which has been created. Primary school children of both sexes have seized on this development and now respond to pop music with the kind of energy often not expanded during other forms of physical education or at any other time in their lives. Teachers should try and harness this energy and enthusiasm when they present country dance lessons within the physical education curriculum. If they do so, they will also be able to fulfil some of the requirements in the National Curriculum, especially having **'opportunities to increase the range and complexity of body actions, including step patterns and use of body parts'** (Programme of Study).

In addition, country dancing lessons enable children to develop two essential cross-curricular requirements, those of health related exercise and professional and social education. What's more, they may also have some fun on the way!

It is important to build on the foundations of the programme which the children will have experienced in Key Stage 1. Once again, however, the initial aim is not necessarily for the children to produce a recognised dance such as 'The dashing white sergeant' or 'The eightsome reel', but to create a dance or dance pattern for themselves.

In this section, the lessons are structured as follows.
• Warm-up: where the children are involved in lots of enjoyable and easily performed movement to a musical accompaniment of some kind.
• Movement training: where children are taught new steps or new movements. As their repertoire increases, the children will eventually be able to use the step or figure in a recognised dance. Each new step or figure should initially be taught without music, so that the children can practise them slowly.
• Dance: where the children experience a 'real dance' even in their first lesson, so that they feel that they have achieved something. Initially, the dance may just be a simple combination of walking or skipping in a circle, but towards the end of Key Stage 2 it could either be a complex dance choreographed by the children or a traditional, recognised country dance. When children are creating their own dances it helps them if you play the music for the dance while they are discussing and practising the various steps and figures. Also, when being taught a recognised, traditional dance, it will help the children to walk through the dance without the music before they attempt to move to the tempo of the dance.
• Cool-down: where the children should walk alone and be guided into calming, slower movements either with or without musical accompaniment. This will help their bodies to adjust to the more sedentary activities in the classroom.

There are eight lessons in this section

which are offered as examples, rather than as a complete scheme. You may want to repeat some of the lessons or part of them for younger children in Key Stage 2. As children reach Year 5 and Year 6 you may decide to extend the children's repertoire of traditional dances, to include dances from other cultures.

Finally, the music used for all these lessons may be chosen from any recognised country dance collection. Contemporary music which has a steady beat is also recommended.

Lesson one
Warm-up

Ask the children to skip around the area to any country dance music. They can then do this again, but this time ask them to stand still and 'freeze' when the music stops.

Movement training

Demonstrate a slip-step to the children as follows:
• take a step to the right and put all your weight on your right foot;
• bring your left foot to join your right foot and put all your weight on your left foot;
• repeat the movement and increase the speed of the action until the weight on the right foot is transferred on to the left foot with a jump. Eventually the sideways slip-step has the same rhythm and springing action as a skipping step.

Let the children practise the slip-step by moving to the right across the room with their right legs leading and then slip-step across the room with their left legs leading their movements.

Finally, ask the children to slip-step in the area making their own pathways and choosing which leg to lead the movement.

Dance

Use the music which the children have been practising to earlier in the lesson, so that they are familiar with it. Ask all the children to hold hands and form a circle and help them to perform the following simple pattern dance:
• take eight slip-steps anticlockwise;
• take 16 slip-steps clockwise;
• drop hands and perform eight slip-steps away from the circle;
• take eight slip-steps to return to the circle and join hands ready to repeat the dance.

Cool-down

Ask the children to stand still and breathe in and then breathe out slowly and with control. They can then walk around the area and lead out, back to the classroom.

Lesson two
Warm-up

Ask the children to walk with a springy step to the music. Tell them to pat the right palms of their hands with the palm of any person passing by them, as they walk to the music.

They can then change to walking on the spot, swinging their arms at their sides. Then ask them to walk around the area again and this time when they meet someone, they can walk on the spot and clap both palms of their hands against the other child's hands before continuing to walk alone.

Movement training

Teach the children how to turn their partner with their right and left arms as follows. They should:
• face their partner;
• adjust their position so that they can link their right arms at the elbow and turn around once until they are back where they started;
• adjust their position and link left arms and turn their partner.

Let the children practise this turn and then walk around the area to the music. When they meet another person they should turn the person with their right arms linked at the elbow before continuing to walk alone. They should also practise this using their left arms and turning anticlockwise. The children can then choose a partner and each pair should face each other, standing two paces apart. Tell them to walk on the spot, still facing their partners. They should then walk to meet their partners, turning their partners with their right elbows linked. Once they have done this they should fall back into their places, and repeat the sequence, but this time linking their left elbows.

Dance

Ask the children to choose partners, and form two circles, one inside the other with each pair facing their partners.

The dance sequence is as follows:
• the children should face their partners and stand two steps away;
• they should walk to meet their partners, link right elbows, turn around once and step back into their starting places;
• tell the children to walk to meet their partners, link left elbows, turn around once and step back into their starting places;
• the children on the inside circle should join hands and walk clockwise for eight steps, while the children on the outer circle, without holding hands, walk in the opposite direction around the circle;
• all the children should stand still after eight steps and face a new partner, ready to start the dance again.

After this lesson you might like to extend and broaden the children's dance activities by letting them use the steps and movements which they have learned with new pieces of music. You can take them through their repertoire to remind them about all the steps and movements which they know and then invite them to make up a dance with their partners. Provide the children with a framework within which to work, for example: make up a dance where each figure is completed to eight beats of the music and choose eight figures to make up the dance and repeat them.

The children can show each other their dances and be encouraged to evaluate each other's performances. They should be guided to comment, for instance, on the patterns in the dance, the figures, the flow of the dance and the performance of the dancers, neat footwork and good body positions.

Cool-down

Ask the children to walk with long stretched strides around the room until you tell them to change. On this command they should walk with a normal upright posture.

Lesson three
Warm-up

Let the children walk, skip or slip-step to the music. Encourage them to move in different directions and to move forwards and backwards.

Ask the children to clap their hands and then to stamp their feet to the beat of the music. They can then nod their heads and point and wag their index fingers to the beat of the music.

Movement training

Teach the children the do-se-do (back to back) movement as follows:
• tell each child to face a partner;
• they should walk towards their partners;
• they should pass their partner's right shoulder;
• tell them to take a step to the right until they are back to back with their partners;
• they should stay facing in the same direction and walk backwards passing their partners' left shoulders;
• they should continue walking backwards until they reach their starting positions.

Let the children practise this movement several times with the music. Once they have grasped the basic technique they can practise it both walking and skipping.

Dance

• Ask each child to find a space and stand four steps away from and facing a partner.
• Each child should walk forward to meet his partner and nod to her and return to his starting position. They should do this twice (16 steps).
• The partners then meet and do-se-do, passing right shoulders, and return to their places. Again they should do this twice (16 steps).
• They should do-se-do again, but this time passing their left shoulders. They should do this twice also (16 steps).
• Ask the partners to walk towards each other and join both hands and walk round in a circle on the spot. They should do this twice, and then drop hands ready to start the dance again (16 steps).

Cool-down

Each pair of children can walk together with good posture one behind the other around the area.

Lesson four

Warm-up

Tell all the children to find a space and stand still. When the music starts each girl should skip around and find a boy partner. Obviously if there is an uneven number of boys and girls you will have to take this into account. Each girl should stand behind her partner and they should skip together, one behind the other until the music stops. The couples should then separate and find a space again. Repeat this sequence, but this time ask the boys to find a female partner.

Another variation of this activity is to let the children stand side by side with their partners and skip around the area together.

Movement training

Teach the children how to turn with a partner using crossed arms style:

• each child should face a partner;
• the pairs then shake right hands and, without loosening their right hand grip, shake left hands;
• keeping this crossed-arm grip, the children should straighten their arms and skip around on the spot through one complete turn.

The children can work up to this turn by practising walking towards their partners, taking the crossed-hands hold, and then releasing it and walking backwards to their starting places. They can repeat this, but this time skipping forwards and skipping on the spot as they grip hands. Once they are fairly competent you can introduce music and let the children practice turning to the right and turning to the left before they return to their starting places.

Dance

Ask the children to choose a partner and form two circles so that each pair are facing each other. Try to use boy/girl partnerships and if so, the boys should make up the outer circle while the girls face them, as the inner circle.
• Ask the girls to skip in a clockwise direction until they are all back in their original places facing their partners.
• Ask the boys to skip in an anticlockwise direction until they return to their starting positions.
• They should then circle as before, but this time both circles move at the same time.
• Once they are back in their original positions each child can skip towards their partners and turn them four times around to the right and then four times to the left.

Cool-down

Ask each couple to walk quietly around the area one behind the other.

Lesson five

Teach the children the 'Virginia reel'.

Warm-up

Ask the children to skip around the area and skip on the spot to the music. They can choose when they will skip on the spot. You can suggest that they skip around for eight skips and then skip on the spot for eight skips.

Tell the children to skip around the area and when the music stops they should all find partners of the opposite sex and skip side by side with them.

The children can then stand side by side with their partners and when the music starts they should both skip forward together for eight steps and then turn away from each other and skip to the place where they started and begin the figure again.

Movement training

Teach the children a left and right hand turn as follows:
• ask the children to stand so that they are two steps away from each other;
• the children should walk towards their partners, bend their right arms at the elbows so that the palms of their hands are at shoulder height and facing the right palms of their partners' hands;
• they should grasp their partners' right hands firmly and keep their hands at shoulder height;
• ask the children to walk around on the spot until they are back in the position in which they started;
• they should also try the turn with their left hands joined.

The children can practise this turn and also the do-se-do with some music.

Dance

Before the children attempt to perform this dance to music they should walk through the figures until they are confident enough to try it to music.
• Arrange the children so that four or five couples stand in a row facing their partners about four steps apart.

• The girls' line and the boys' line should walk towards each other, nod and walk backwards back to their places. They should do this twice.
• Both lines walk towards each other again, and this time each couple completes a right hand turn followed by a left hand turn, before stepping back into their original starting positions.
• Each couple then completes a two-handed turn.
• Ask each couple to complete a do-se-do, passing right shoulders, and then returning to their starting places.
• The top couple should then join both hands facing each other, and slip-step sideways between both lines for eight steps to the end of the line and then return to their starting position with eight more slip-steps.
• The top couple then drop hands and the boy turns away from his partner and leads all the boys to the bottom of the line. At the same time, the top girl turns away and leads all the girls to the bottom of the line, returning to the top of the line once more and making an arch.
• Each couple then meets their partner and goes under the arch in turn.
• Once all the couples have been through the arch they should walk back and stand in the original formation of each line facing the other.

Cool-down

Ask the children to lie down on their backs and stretch their whole bodies. Tell them to stand up again, making sure they stand correctly.

Lesson six

Teach the children the 'Pat-a-cake polka'.

Warm-up

Tell the children to jump on two feet on the spot to the music. They can then skip around the area choosing children with whom to turn. They can choose whether to link right or left elbows as they turn or to take the other person's hand at shoulder height to make the turn. Encourage them to skip freely and to try both left and right turns.

Movement training

Ask the children to work with a partner. Tell each pair to stand side by side with their partners and practise tapping the toes of their outside feet on the floor while they jump on their inside feet. Let them practise tapping the heels of their outside feet on the floor while they jump on their inside feet. They can then try both of these with the music.

Let the children practise tapping first their toes and then their heels as they jump. Also let the children practise slip-stepping to the right with their right leg leading and then slip-stepping to the left with their left leg leading. They should face their partners and without touching each other, practise slip-stepping together, first in one direction and then in the other. Finally, they can try this with the music.

Also tell the children to face their partners and practise clapping the palms of each other's hands.

Dance

• Ask the children to choose partners and form two circles – with all the boys standing on the inside circle and all the girls standing on the outside circle (if they are in mixed pairs). Each child should stand beside his or her partner and all the couples should face in an anticlockwise direction.
• Tell the children to hold hands and jump on their inside feet (the one nearest to their partners) and tap their toes on the floor and then their heels, and repeat.
• The children should then join both hands and slip-step together in an anticlockwise direction for four steps.
• Ask the children to turn so that the pairs are standing side by side and everyone is facing in a clockwise direction, and repeat the jumping and toe and heel tapping as

before. They should then take four slip-steps together in a clockwise direction.
• Each couple should face their partners again and clap their right hands three times, their left hands three times, and then both hands three times.
• Ask each child on the outside circle to move one place to the left to face a new partner and then the couples can turn their new partners using a crossed-arms hold.

Cool-down

Let the children use stretching movements, using first their right arms and then their left arms, to trace the letters of their own name in the air. They can then use first their right feet and then their left feet to trace their own names on the floor. This can be made more pleasurable if you play a piece of music which has a quiet and calming mood.

Lesson seven

Teach the children 'The Oxo reel'.

Warm-up

• Ask the children to skip around the area to the music and when you call out a number, everyone should skip until the children have formed groups each of the chosen number of individuals. The assembled groups of children should join hands and skip in circles until you call out 'scatter', when they should skip alone again.
• Ask the children to walk briskly to the music and practise changing from moving forwards, to moving backwards, to walking on the spot, as you call out 'forwards', 'backwards' or 'on the spot'.

Movement training

Teach the children to make a right- and left-hand star as follows:
• ask two boys to stand side by side and face two girls;
• each boy should hold the hand of the girl

who is not his partner in the same way as if he were to make a right-hand turn.

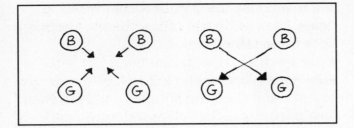

• the four children should keep a firm grip and walk around clockwise in a circle until they return to their starting positions;
• the four children then change hands so that they use their left hands and walk around in an anticlockwise direction.

Let the children practise walking around in a right-hand star, followed by a left-hand star with the music.

Once the children have practised making a star they can extend their practice to include slip-stepping to the right and then slip-stepping to the left along a straight line. Ask the children to slip-step to the right for three steps, change direction for one step and slip-step to the left for four steps.

They can also practise a right-hand turn and a left-hand turn with a partner, to the music (eight steps) and walk forwards to meet their partners and walk away from their partners backwards (eight steps).

Dance

• Ask the children to stand with their partners in groups of four couples so that they make two lines.
• Tell the boys to join hands at shoulder height and form a line and ask the girls to form a similar line and face the boys.
• Each line should skip (or walk) forwards to meet their partners and skip (or walk) backwards to their starting places.
• Each girl and boy then move forward to meet each other and complete a right-hand turn.
• Again, each line should walk forwards and back to meet their partners followed by a left-hand turn.

• Ask the top couple and the bottom couple to turn using their left and then their right hands, while the two middle couples complete a right-hand star followed by a left-hand star.
• The top couple take a crossed-hands hold and move down the set between the two lines of dancers turning around and around as they skip. When they reach the end of the set, they form the new bottom couple and the dance can start again.

Cool-down

Ask the children to sit on the floor and stretch their legs and feet out in front of them. They should stretch their arms wide and keep their spines and heads erect. Finally, ask them to stand maintaining a good posture.

Lesson eight

Teach the children a stick dance. The children will each need a piece of broomstick about the length of a relay baton for this dance.

Warm-up

Play the music which will be used for the stick dance so that the children can try and pick up the rhythm. Any morris dance music will be suitable, as well as some contemporary music such as 'Too many broken hearts' sung by Jason Donovan. Play the music and let the children practise clapping their hands to the beat of the music.

Movement training

Teach the children the polka sequence of steps as follows:
• the children should take three steps forwards: left, right, left and hop on their left foot keeping their right foot in the air;
• step backwards with their right feet, step backwards with their left feet, step backwards on their right feet and hop on them, keeping their left feet in the air.

The children should work on this step sequence without the music before practising it with the music. They can then introduce a quarter turn to their left after they hop on their left feet. By making a turn they should be able to move around the area.

You can then introduce the children to the idea of carrying a stick while they make these patterns. They should also practise tapping their sticks against a partner's stick eight times.

Dance

• Ask the children to join into groups of four couples and stand so that the boys are lined up one behind the other next to the girls who have made a similar line. All the children face the front of the area.

• All the children should hold their sticks in

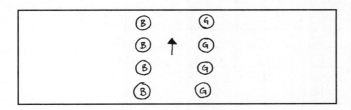

their right hands and advance and retreat together twice using the polka step (16 steps).

• On the last hop the children should turn to face their partners.

• Each boy and girl must advance with their line towards each other and return to their starting place twice (16 steps).

• Each boy and girl then taps their partner's stick 15 times and on the last beat turns to face the front again.

• The top couple then 'cast-off' by turning away from their partners and, using the polka step, move forwards.

• The top boy and girl then lead and the other boys and girls follow them as they move down the line.

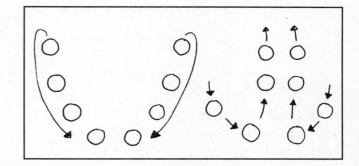

When the top couple reach the bottom of their line they must stand still while the others go through them meeting their partners in turn and returning to the top of the line, so that a new couple are at the top of the line and ready to start again.

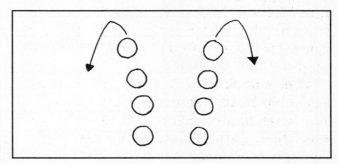

Cool-down

Ask the children to stand still and try to balance on one foot while they stretch their other leg and foot out in front of their bodies. Finally, they can practise walking while maintaining a good posture.

Evaluation sheet
Dance Key Stage 2

	Name								Comments
Creative dance									
• Physical skills co-ordination									
good line									
• Ability effective expression									
consistent									
adaptable									
creative									
• Planning and organisation imaginative performance									
clear actions									
solves tasks									
creates dances with clear beginnings, middles and ends									
• Evaluation selects key features									
uses functional criteria									
uses aesthetic criteria									
Country dance									
• Physical skills co-ordination									
skip									
slip-step									
polka									
• Ability rhythmic response									
completes figures accurately									
• Planning and organisation creates dances with clear beginnings, middles and ends									
• Evaluation uses functional criteria									
makes appropriate comparisons with other performances									

Chapter 10

Outdoor and adventurous activities

'Pupils should:
- **be taught the principles of safety in the outdoors and develop the ability to assess and respond to challenges in a variety of contexts and conditions.**
- **experience outdoor and adventurous activities in different environments *(such as school grounds and premises, parks, woodlands or sea shore)* that involve planning, navigation, working in small groups, recording and evaluating.**
- **be taught the skills necessary for the activity undertaken with due regard for safety including the correct use of appropriate equipment.'**
(Programme of Study).

The principal features of this programme for Key Stage 2 are twofold. First, it is recommended that outdoor and adventurous activities should give children the opportunity to sample the excitement of physical situations beyond the school environment, but also in natural settings which may be some distance from where they live. The implication of this is that teachers will have to organise visits to these places. Some teachers might wish to include visits which incorporate an overnight experience. There are many outdoor activity centres and youth hostels which can cater for the needs of an outdoor physical challenge.

Second, is the importance of safety, particularly since children are seldom naturally cautious. All outdoor physical activity contains an element of risk and consequently safety principles cannot be taken lightly, especially when activities,

173

though teacher-supervised, may not be teacher-led. Any programme, therefore, which ignores instructing children about safe practice and potential hazards does so at its peril!

This chapter examines the possibilities for delivering this area of the National Curriculum both in the immediate locality of the school and in the other recommended environments. Eight activities are suggested, seven of which could be undertaken by teachers without specialist qualifications in outdoor activity work. These activities are suitable for all children in Key Stage 2 and do not require any specialised skills from the children, other than those needed for any usual school physical education programme. Some children with certain special needs may need additional assistance, but no more than would be required in school.

The eight activities are: outdoor pursuits at a residential centre; hiking and a youth hostel experience; outdoor activities in the school grounds; navigational skills in the immediate environment; navigational skills and physical activity in woodlands; navigational skills and physical activity at the seashore; fell walking and an assault course.

The most useful publications to consult before you take the children out of school are probably the DES booklets *Learning out-of-doors* (1985, HMSO) and *Safety in Outdoor Education* (1989, HMSO) or any equivalent LEA document. You should also read the information on outdoor pursuits given in the BAALPE book *Safe Practice in Physical Education* (1990) (NB Chapter 5 pp. 83–103).

Inevitably, the emphasis in all this literature is on ensuring safety, but usually in the context of maintaining the spirit of adventure for the children.

Structuring activities involves considerable preliminary planning by the teacher. A visit to the new area or terrain before the 'expedition' begins is essential and there is no doubt that those teachers who have had some experience of the activities which they choose to share with children are likely to be those who will

conduct the 'safest' adventures. This checklist will help any teachers who are doubtful about their competence to lead a school party, together with information concerning the organisational requirements for out-of-doors activities.

• Has the trip been thoroughly organised and prepared, covering all details such as clothing, food and rest periods?
• Is the teacher-pupil ratio appropriate to the planned activity? Consider the nature of the activity; the degree of danger likely; the experience and expertise of the staff and the ages and competence of the pupils.
• Is there a schedule for continuous supervision?
• Will there be at least one teacher with each group who is trained in first aid, including resuscitation methods and treatment for exposure?
• Have potential weather conditions been taken into account (particularly in winter)?
• Is there appropriate and adequate insurance cover, including health cover and cover for teachers' own vehicles when conveying pupils?
• Have parents been informed and signed the appropriate consent forms? Draft parental consent forms can be found in the booklet *Safety in Outdoor Education*, (1989).

Outdoor pursuits at a residential outdoor centre

One of the finest experiences which we can give children is a visit to a specialist, residential, outdoor pursuits centre. The value of such a visit is that most of the centres have qualified staff who have extensive knowledge and experience in leading and teaching groups of children about the skills required to take part in a whole range of activities such as canoeing, sailing, orienteering, windsurfing, fell walking, rock climbing and so on. The centres also stock the correct equipment and clothing for the children to use for each of the activities. Staff in such centres know various ways of showing children how to follow safety and country codes, but most importantly they know how to develop children's self-esteem and aesthetic awareness as they enjoy themselves outdoors, achieving new goals. Wherever possible children should spend at least a few days once in their school lives at one of these centres.

Hiking and a youth hostel experience

There is little doubt that children in Key Stage 2 will relish at least an overnight stay in a youth hostel, simply because it will seem like a great adventure! Most will enjoy sleeping away from home and being with school friends rather than with family. This kind of experience makes a valuable contribution to the the aim of outdoor education which is concerned with their personal and social development.

Youth hostelling activities could include fell walking and navigation in woodlands or at the seashore (outlined later in the chapter); activities which could be explored over one or two days.

For some schools and for some children, however, staying at an outdoor pursuits centre or youth hostel may not be possible, often for economic reasons. If this is the case, consider what other opportunities can be provided for the children in order that they can **'experience outdoor and adventurous activities in different environments (such as school grounds and prmises, parks, woodlands or sea shore) that involve planning, navigation, working in small groups, recording and evaluation'** (Programme of Study).

Outdoor activities in the school grounds

Children in Key Stage 2 should have the opportunity to be physically active in their own school grounds at play times and dinner time each day in the manner which was suggested for Key Stage 1 children (see pages 81–83). Key Stage 2 children could, however, take a greater interest in the school environment and developing these kinds of activities by making a plan for a more adventurous playground. To do this, the children should be organised into groups and encouraged to discuss their ideas and to make a plan of the proposed layout. They could then make drawings and models of their selected equipment, considering costs, viability and the safety aspects of their proposals. They could also suggest why they had chosen the various pieces of equipment and which types of physical activity they thought children might perform on the equipment.

The recent DES booklet, *Playground Safety Guidelines* (1992), covers all the necessary considerations when permanent play equipment is to be installed in the school grounds.

Navigational skills in the immediate environment

Older primary school children should become involved in planning an orienteering route in the very immediate neighbourhood of their school. In order to do this, a class can be divided into groups and each group asked to devise a route which another group could then follow.

Initially it might be difficult for the children to judge distances and to relate those distances represented on the plan to the physical reality of moving over the terrain. Nevertheless, it will provide the children with an important first step in eventually being able to find their way using a map and compass.

To develop this orienteering route activity each group of children will need to make paper flags of a distinctive colour and size to mark their routes outdoors, and would also need to draw the location of their flags on their route maps. Other symbols such as bus stops, telephone boxes and shops could be marked on the plan to help the navigators find their way. A key of the symbols should be clearly shown at the bottom of the map.

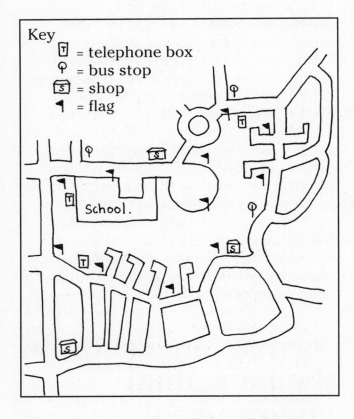

Help the children to develop this early planning by asking them to consider how various people find their way across different terrains. For example, you might pose the following sorts of questions:
• 'How does a mountaineer find her way around the mountains?'
• 'How will submarine commanders find their way under the sea?'

The children should also be shown the basic methods of navigation using a compass, first within the classroom and then within the school grounds. Clearly this kind of work could be incorporated into work connected with geographical and historical topics associated with explorers such as Captain Cook, Bartholomew Diaz, Vasco da Gama, Sherpa Tensing, Christopher Columbus or Dr Livingstone.

It is obvious from the above activity that physical education integrates very effectively with some aspects of the geography curriculum. In both areas there is overlap, for example, following directions, using a compass, making maps and using Ordnance Survey maps. Similarly, in physical education and geography, children are required to investigate other locations so that they can look at different features, such as water in its various forms, and be able to identify and describe various landscape features, for example, rivers, hills, valleys and lakes, through direct and practical experience.

Navigation skills and physical activity in woodlands

In order to learn **'the principles of safety in the outdoors and develop the ability to assess and respond to challenges in a variety of contexts and conditions'** (Programme of Study) it will be necessary to make a visit to another locality. However, before the visit the children should be made aware of what they are going to do in the woodlands once they get there. They should look at the type of clothing and footwear they will need and any training which might be necessary. You should also discuss with them which safety rules might be appropriate.

When thinking about this sort of activity it is necessary to try and plan the following:
• some uphill climbing on various terrains, such as grassy banks and rocks;
• some jogging through high plantations, for example, bracken covered valleys, and bush surrounded pathways;
• walking down steep, tree covered hills;
• manoeuvring around, under or over natural obstacles such as branches, logs, streams, rocks;
• coping with bogs and marshes;
• negotiating man-made obstacles such as fences, walls, paths and stiles.

The following activities are therefore suggested to illustrate what might be done in a woodland environment.

Orientation activities

Plan a route of about three kilometres which you and the children can enjoy completing together. The route should include as many of the activities outlined above as possible.

Tracking

Mark a route through the woodlands using brightly coloured flags and let the children try to follow it. Care should be taken, when 'planting' these flags, so that the environment is not damaged in any way. Each flag should be placed so that it can be seen easily as the children move from flag to flag. The children can work in groups, setting off at two minute intervals.

Navigation

Make a 'map' of a route through the woodland and give copies to pairs of children. The map should show pathways and important features such as a clearing, a set of steps or a stream. Place brightly coloured flags along the route and mark them on the map. These flags can then be used as check points, so that the children will be able to tell whether they are following the correct route. For this navigation activity it is important that other flags can not be seen from the various points so that the children have to rely on their maps.

Mapping

The children should be organised into groups of three or four and be given the task of creating a route and a map for another group to follow. When each map is completed, you should check it thoroughly before allowing another group to use it.

Navigational skills and physical activity at the seashore

Activities which take place in, near, or above the seashore have great potential for a range of sensory and aesthetic experiences. Another valuable consequence of such activities is that it gives children the knowledge and confidence to enjoy what could be a potentially hazardous environment. It is important to remember, too, that the hazards are not always 'natural'. Any beach nowadays frequently displays the results of damage to our natural environment. Often it takes the more visible form of rubbish washed up by the tide or simply deposited by an unthinking general public, but sometimes it can be that almost invisible detritus caused by unseen chemical effluents and pollution. The teacher should, therefore, make the children aware that any visit to the beach, while potentially invigorating, can also have hidden dangers which they must recognise. None the less, it provides children with the ideal opportunity to 'test' their developing physical skills in situations where there is sometimes risk and a little danger. In such circumstances, it is important that whatever activities you choose for the children should range from those which are initially safe, confidence-building and manageable to those where there is some challenge and a consequent feeling of physical and emotional satisfaction once the challenge has been overcome. At a later stage, and as the children develop, they should be encouraged to choose their own levels of participation and their own 'adventure thresholds'.

Try the following activities with the children or arrange similar excursions.
• Plan a route for a beach or cliff walk so that the children have some experience of walking up and down a cliff path, negotiating narrow pathways, pushing past sea holly, walking across wet and dry sand,

and in and out of sand-dunes. The children will enjoy negotiating the moving terrain in the sand dunes and feeling the extra strength needed in their legs to walk uphill. They will undoubtedly enjoy the undulation of the dunes and the loss of immediate sight of their friends as each moves into the next hollow.

• Give the children the opportunity to climb up, on and over any large rocks which are situated on the beach, or which form a rocky outcrop or promontory on the edge of and into the sea. They should be given the freedom to move about on the rocks so that each individual can choose her own challenges and move about according to her own motor skill ability.

Fell walking

Fell walking is a very popular leisure activity for many people and is an activity which teachers and children can both enjoy together. As children are introduced to fell walking for the first time, make sure that the whole journey across the hills is not too demanding. Choose a lowland route and make sure that all the children walk at the pace of the slowest child. The first 'mountain' walk should not be longer than four miles and should seem adventurous without causing too much stress.

The route should take the children up and down at least one steep hill so that they can begin to cope with the demands of distributing their body weight on steep inclines on the downward route as well as the upward route. They can be shown how important it is to maintain a steady rhythm and pace as they climb up the hill and also how important it is to breathe correctly, breathing in as they step on one foot, and breathing out as they step on the other. The route should go over various terrains such as rocks, marshes, stepping stones over streams, under low branches, through thickets and through a wood. The route should also include some negotiation of stiles, fences and gates so that the children can begin to learn about the country code,

closing gates, using stiles properly and not damaging walls and fences by climbing over in the wrong places.

Children can be taken on a more demanding route each year, culminating where possible with an opportunity to 'climb a mountain'.

Military assault courses

Some schools are situated reasonably near to military bases where access to an assault course might be possible. Military assault courses can be very challenging for older primary school children and can provide a valuable outdoor activity experience. Should the military personnel become involved in any visit to one of their assault courses then the children would undoubtedly learn something about organisation and discipline!

Recording and assessing

In addition to recording each child's attainments in outdoor and adventurous activities, you should also note the type and duration of any activities experienced outside school. This will provide essential information both for each child's school profile document and for his specialist Key Stage 3 physical education teacher. The photocopiable evaluation sheet which follows can be adapted as required.

Each child should have her own evaluation sheet, placed in her personal record of achievement file. During the four years the children are in junior school this should be used as a cumulative document, finally becoming a summative record on transferring to Key Stage 3. It is important, therefore, that entries are dated. For simplicity, try using a recognisable recording 'code' together with a detailed comment where appropriate.

Evaluation sheet

Outdoor and adventurous activities Key Stage 2

Name: _____

• Skills	Attainment				Teacher comments and date
	Y3	Y4	Y5	Y6	
Concern and respect for the environment					
Copes with the physical demands of outdoor activities					
Can read and use a route plan					
Can plan routes in co-operation with others					
Can lead others					
Listens and accepts other people's ideas					
Understands safety rules.					
Understands the Country Code					
Understands the physical demands of activities, and their effect on the body					

• Activities in the local environment   Comments

School grounds

Local environment

• Activities experienced in other locations

Outdoor pursuits at a residential centre
Date:
Location:
Duration of visit:
Size of group:
Activities:

Youth hostel experience
Date:
Location:
Duration of visit:
Size of group:
Activities:

Woodlands
Date:
Location:
Duration of visit:
Size of group:
Activities:

Seashore
Date:
Location:
Duration of visit:
Size of group:
Activities:

Other
Date:
Location:
Duration of visit:
Size of group:
Activities:

Key Stages 1 and 2

Chapter 11
Swimming

The statutory order relating to the provision of swimming within the physical education curriculum differs in two ways from the other five areas of provision, in that:
• the introduction of the order will not be immediate, but will be staggered over several years;
• schools are free to choose whether they teach swimming during Key Stage 1 or Key Stage 2, or across both key stages.

However, the end of Key Stage 2 statement is very specific when it states that:

'By the end of the key stage pupils should be able to swim unaided at least 25 metres and demonstrate an understanding of water safety.'

Unquestionably, swimming is a crucial survival skill and an essential prerequisite for participation in a whole range of activities in and around water. Swimming has also become a very popular leisure activity and it could be claimed that it

provides one of the best types of all-round exercise in terms of enhanced flexibility, strength, speed and stamina.

If swimming is taught in Key Stage 1 teaching of the early parts of the programme of study set out in Key Stage 2 should be considered first.

'Pupils should:
• learn and know the codes of hygiene and courtesy for using swimming pools.
• be given opportunities to develop confidence in water; be taught how to rest in water, how to float and to adopt support positions.
• be taught a variety of means of propulsion using either arms or legs or both, and develop effective and efficient swimming strokes on front and back.
• be taught water safety and the principles of water safety to assess the nature, visibility and location of water hazards in a variety of conditions.
• learn survival skills appropriate to their competence in water and evaluate their

own abilities and limitations.
• be encouraged to assess their swimming and water skills efficiency against a range of criteria.
• explore the elements of movement in the water through simple games.
• be made aware of the role of swimming and water safety skills in supporting other water-based activities and activities near water' (*NCC Consultation Report*, 1991).

In order that teachers can retain some flexibility over when they choose or are able to teach children to swim according to the above programme of study the Secretary of State cautions on two important points:
• whenever pupils are taught to swim early in their primary school careers, teachers should ensure that they retain their ability to swim throughout Key Stage 2;
• that pupils in Key Stage 1 may be less able to appreciate the points made about water safety required in the statement of attainment.

Consequently, teachers are reminded that if children are taught to swim during Key Stage 1, and if they can swim at least 25m, then teachers must both ensure that they are still able to swim at the end of Key Stage 2, and that the principles about water safety are reinforced and updated in Key Stage 2.

A large number of primary schools already provide swimming lessons for their children as part of the curriculum. For safety reasons alone, teachers have always recognised that swimming is an important life skill and that it is not only an enjoyable activity, but an activity which opens up access to many water sports outside school time.

This chapter is based around the recommendations listed in the programme of study. Each recommendation is taken in sequence so that, whether you decide to teach swimming during Key Stage 1 or Key Stage 2, the same order of presentation will apply.

Finally, there is another difference between swimming and the other activities in the physical education curriculum. Many children visit their local swimming pools with their own class and their own class teacher, but others will receive instruction from a *specialist* swimming teacher from outside the school. Therefore, unlike other areas of the curriculum a large number of class teachers may not be responsible for teaching some parts of the programme of study for swimming. Nevertheless, it will be the class teacher's responsibility to ensure that the programme of study is implemented and all teachers will be responsible for ensuring that their children are made aware of the curriculum recommendations.

Codes of hygiene and courtesy

It is important that matters of hygiene and courteous practice are discussed with the children before they visit the swimming pool. This information should subsequently be reinforced after they have made their first and subsequent visits.

Children should also be shown how they can play their part in keeping the pool clean and what the rules are for acceptable behaviour.

Hygiene

Before entering the pool area children should:
• remove from their mouths all sweets and chewing gum;
• visit the toilet;
• blow their noses;
• wear a clean swimming costume;
• wear a swim hat if they have long hair;
• wash their feet thoroughly;
• shower their bodies.

Ensuring that these hygiene procedures are observed will require a certain amount of vigilance on your part and you should exclude from the pool any child who has catarrh, a sore throat, a foot infection or any kind of open sore and explain why this is necessary.

Courtesy

When in or beside the pool all children should be given the following rules which they must follow the whole time. They should:
• follow the normal rules of polite behaviour;
• not run or push anyone;
• not raise their voices;
• arrange their clothes tidily in the baskets or cubicles provided;
• not walk on the poolside in outdoor shoes.

Safety

A swimming pool is obviously a place of potential danger and class teachers must take every precaution to ensure the children's safety. It is important to:
• ensure good discipline at all times;
• forbid running or pushing on the poolside;
• not allow the children to enter the water until permission is given;
• make sure the children know and respond quickly to signals to stop, stand still, and to get out of the water;
• check the number of children regularly;
• be acquainted with normal emergency requirements;
• know the location of first aid equipment and the telephone;
• never enter the pool when responsible for a class of children.

A further *recommended* safety requirement for class teachers who are involved in teaching swimming is to gain the Amateur Swimming Association/Royal Life Saving Society Teachers' Life Saving Certificate. Local addresses and information on courses are available from the Sports Council (see Resources). It is essential that someone holding a relevant and current life saving certificate is present at the poolside during *all* swimming lessons. The life saving qualification is purely a rescue qualification and therefore, in addition, it is *recommended* that class teachers who will be teaching swimming should also hold a teacher's certificate awarded by the Amateur Swimming Association or the Swimming Teachers' Association, or at least have attended a swimming course which has been recognised by their LEA. LEA guidelines vary from region to region and therefore anyone who is intending to teach swimming should be thoroughly acquainted with the particular requirements of their LEA.

Schools can play an important role in ensuring that the pool which their children visit is conducive to learning the skills stated in the programme of study. The Amateur Swimming Association has been able to show, for instance, that the suitability of the pool and the water temperature are strongly linked to success in learning to swim. They also recommend that beginners should be taught in learner pools with shallow water, where they have exclusive use of the space. If these conditions are met then the children will quickly gain confidence in the water. Schools should therefore check on both the type of pool and the ambient temperature before allowing their children to begin to be instructed in the programme of study. If the conditions are favourable then the children can progress to the next curriculum recommendation.

Gaining confidence in water and learning to swim

If the conditions of the pool are conducive, then the children will soon be able to fulfil the requirements of being able to rest, float and adopt a support position in water. Having gained this confidence, they will be ready to move on to the next, and most important, stage of learning to swim.

Helping the children to feel confident in the water is crucial if they are to feel happy in the water. You should play an important role in this procedure because it is the class teacher who knows the children better than anyone (other than the children's parents) and will be much more capable of taking the children through the first sensitive stages of introducing them to water and to water activities.

Introductory water activities in a learner pool

A learner pool is by far the best way to introduce children to water activities, especially if we want them to feel happy and secure both with the notion of a pool and also with water and its properties. Learner pools are usually smaller than normal-sized pools and are constructed in two distinct styles:

• a square pool which has a constant water depth of 30–45cm with one side of the pool usually constructed to allow multiple entry by shallow steps or a slope which runs the whole length of that side;

• an oblong pool with two depths of water, one third of the pool deep (120cm) and two thirds shallow (60cm); usually with four entry points consisting of vertical steps at each corner.

In the pools which have a uniform depth it will be possible to teach the early stages of swimming to children by the 'shallow water method'. However, in the other type of learner pool where the water is deeper even at the shallow end, some of the activities which children can practise in very shallow water may have to be omitted.

The following activities, presented as a sequence, are suggested as a means of encouraging children to be confident in water. Some of these activities are not suitable for learner pools where the shallow end is deeper than 45cm.

• Let the children practise stepping into the pool and out again. (The method of entry into other types of pool is described on page 186.)

• Ask the children to stand in the water, bend their knees and wet their bottoms.

• Tell the children to wet different parts of their bodies with their hands.

• Ask the children to run water up and down their arms, legs and tummies.

• Ask the children to walk around the pool while they hold the trough or rail around the poolside.

• Let them play freely with a plastic toy, ball, container or watering can.

• Tell the children to splash their hands on the surface of the water.

• If the pool is very shallow, ask the children if they can sit down in the water.

• Ask the children if they can lift one leg out of the water.

• Ask the children to use both hands to wash their faces with the water.

• Let the children practise holding the trough or rail with both hands and jumping up and down in the water.

• Ask the children if they can hold on to the trough with one hand and bend down and touch the bottom of the pool with the other without being submerged.

• Ask the children to walk across the pool.

Often children gain water confidence more quickly if they are motivated by a friend, so they will probably enjoy working with partners on some of the following activities.

• Ask each child to stand with his back to the poolside and face his partner who stands at the opposite end of the pool with her back to the poolside. Can the children walk across the pool to meet each other and then walk back again? Can they walk across the pool and clap hands with their partners? Can they walk across the whole pool, passing their partners, and then wave to their partners from the other end? Can they walk to meet their partners, joining both hands and turning around on the spot? Can they stand still holding their partners' hands while their partners jump up and down in the water?

• Ask the children to stand behind their partners, placing their hands on their partners' shoulders. They can then move about the pool together.

• Tell each child to face his partner, standing about 1m away from her. One child should hold a ping-pong ball and, taking a deep breath, blow the ball across the water towards his partner.

• Ask the children to face their partners, standing about 2m apart, and practise walking quickly around their partners and back to their starting positions. Encourage them to use each of their hands in turn to pull the water as they walk. Tell them also to bend their knees when they walk and concentrate on balancing.

As the children's confidence increases they can try out some of the following suggestions.

• Ask them to practise pushing the water using the palms of their hands with a downward movement. They can also try pulling the water from in front of their bodies and along the sides of their bodies, using one hand after the other.

• Let them splash with their hands, making the water move in different directions.

• If you are in a very shallow pool, tell them to put both their hands on the bottom of the pool and then crawl along the bottom on their hands and knees.

• Encourage them to put both their hands on the bottom of the pool and, after taking a deep breath, close their eyes and their mouths and, without breathing, put their faces in the water. When they have done this several times they could try blowing the air out while their faces are in the water to make bubbles and opening their eyes to look at their hands.

• Ask them to put their hands and feet on the bottom of the pool and then gently lift one leg off the bottom. Can they then move about the pool?

• Encourage them to take a deep breath, close their mouths, put their heads into the water and hum a tune.

• Ask them to take a deep breath, close their mouths, put their heads into the water and blow out all the air into the water, then come up and do it again.

• Encourage them to put their hands flat on the bottom of the pool, with their fronts and then backs towards the bottom of the pool, so that their chins are on the water. They should then stretch their bodies, lifting both legs off the bottom of the pool and propel themselves along by walking on their hands with their legs floating behind them. (Some children will propel themselves so confidently that their arms will begin to move in a sort of dog-paddle action.)

Remember, with all these activities, children will feel safest in shallower water (30–45cm) because they will be able to regain their upright positions easily by kneeling down and then standing up.

Introductory water activities in a normal-sized pool

Unfortunately, conditions may not be ideal for attempting some of the activities listed above. For example, some children may be faced with the task of learning to swim in a larger pool where the water will be considerably deeper than in a learner pool. If this is the case, then you must remember that learners who cannot swim must never be taken into water that is deeper than their mid-chest height. Also some children may need additional buoyancy aids to help them develop confidence. There are various aids which are suitable for this purpose, the most popular being arm bands and oblong floats. You should select the ones that seem to be the most suitable for the activity the children are doing and ensure that, where appropriate, they are both properly inflated and secured before allowing any child to enter the pool.

When children use a normal-sized pool for the first time, they should first of all be shown where the area of deep water begins and where the shallow water is located. It adds to safe practice, too, if a coloured rope can be suspended across the pool to mark the beginning of the deep water. The children should also be shown how a whistle will be used as a signal to tell them to stop, look and listen during the course of all lessons.

The children should line up and be shown individually how to enter the water using the steps. Each child should turn so that her back is facing the water and, facing the poolside, she should hold the hand rails firmly and place each foot carefully on the steps as she descends. Once the children are in the water, they should walk along with their feet on the bottom of the pool, keeping close to the side walls. Suggest to them that they can use one hand to hold the rail and one hand to help them balance. Each child should follow the one in front until they are all in the water and holding the rail along two sides of the pool. This method of entry is by far the safest, and will be the method used by *many* non-swimmers during the course of their initial lessons.

Some children, however, will become confident quickly and so in later lessons they should be shown how to get into the pool without using the steps. This can be accomplished by asking the children to sit down on the poolside with their feet in the trough and then, by getting them to grasp the rail with one hand and turn their bodies sideways, they will be able to grasp the rail with their other hand. When they have

done this, they can then transfer their body weight on to their hands and drop gently into the water.

As soon as all the children are in the water and evenly spread out along two sides of the pool, you should help them to warm up. Suggest that they face the poolside, grasp the rail with both hands and gently bend their knees until their shoulders are under the water. They should do this many times, as quickly as possible, for maximum benefit.

Children who have worked in a shallow-water pool and who are experiencing deeper water for the first time should be helped to understand their new environment by carrying out some of the practices listed earlier in the chapter.

The children should now be ready to learn how the water will support their bodies and be taught how to swim one of the recognised strokes. There are three important factors to be considered in learning to swim:
• body position;
• breathing;
• propulsion.

The correct breathing technique for each stroke is an essential requirement if the swimmer is to achieve the correct body position in the water and consequently be able to propel his body proficiently. The exception, however, is the breaststroke as will be shown later in the chapter.

The following activities are suggested to help the children understand the three factors mentioned above.
• Ask the children to bend their knees so that their shoulders are in the water with their chins resting on the surface. In this position, ask them to walk across the pool, in the shallow water, to the other side.
• Initially the children will need to hold the rail with both hands in order to practise breathing out into the water. Let them try taking a deep breath, closing their mouths and their eyes and putting their faces into the water, counting to three and then lifting their faces out again. They can repeat this but this time blow the air into the water before lifting their faces out again. Can they

also open their eyes in the water? Can they hum a tune? They should try all these activities while holding the rail with one hand and then without holding the rail.

Having completed these practices successfully you can encourage the children to play a game in the middle of the pool in the shallow water. Ask the children to join hands in a circle and give each child a number. When you call 'evens' those children with an even number should bend their knees until their heads go under the water, count to three and then lift their heads out again. If you call 'odd' these children should do the same. Remember to tell the children to take a deep breath in, and to close their mouths and eyes before they duck under the water!

The children can then start to work on activities which will help them to experience the sensation of letting the water support their weight and trying to assume a prone position in the water.
• Ask the children to stand facing the pool wall from just over a stretched arm's distance away and in a lunge position.

From this position the children should lean forward on to the water, push off with their feet and glide forward to grasp the rail.
• Encourage the children to stand further and further away as they increase their confidence until eventually they can let both legs glide on top of the water as they reach for the rail.
• Teach the children how to stand up from a prone position.

• Let the children practise towing each other across the pool.
• Give the children a float each and let them practise crossing the pool by kicking their legs in a scissor action.

As soon as you have observed that the children know the water will support their bodies and that the movement of their limbs can propel their bodies through the water, you will be able to begin to teach the children the recognised swimming strokes.

Teaching swimming strokes

Specialist swimming teachers will normally follow the teaching syllabus as laid out in the official handbooks of the Amateur Swimming Association and Swimming Teachers Association (see Resources) when teaching children the fundamental swimming strokes. The ASA also publishes a coaching guide called *Swimming Teaching and Coaching Level 1* (1991) which is invaluable for specialists and also a 'primary pack' which is useful for class teachers.

The information which follows is intended to provide class teachers with a guide as to how to begin to teach the four fundamental strokes. Each stroke is taught within a lesson consisting of three parts.
• Warm-up: in the early stages of learning

to swim the children will need to be directed to do such activities as holding the rail and jumping up and down, or when some children will be able to swim, to swim four to ten widths using their favourite stroke.

• Skill learning: this part of the lesson will be devoted to teaching the four fundamental strokes as and when individuals and/or groups are ready to receive instruction. Having taught the strokes, this part of the lesson will be used to improve the children's techniques and improve their stamina. Eventually some children will be keen to practise swimming at speed, and some children will practise survival activities.

At this point the children may need to be divided into ability groups if each child is to make progress. The pool should therefore be divided into three areas:
– learners in the shallow water area;
– new swimmers in the middle of the pool;
– swimmers in the deep water area.

In each lesson you should let one of the children provide a good demonstration of the whole stroke. You should also offer some arm stroke and leg stroke practices, and offer some help with breathing practices. Try to give individual tuition during every lesson, encouraging the less-able children to try to swim the whole stroke and encouraging improving swimmers to swim further.

• Cool-down: after the more intensive teaching of the previous part of the lesson the children should be allowed to have some fun in a less structured format. They can play a game together in the shallow water and practise their favourite strokes or practise swimming 25m. You could also teach the children a swimming 'stunt' such as sculling with their hands while swimming on their backs or spinning around in the water in a tucked position.

The warm-up and cool-down are important parts of the swimming lesson, but it is not proposed to dwell on what should be taught in these areas, instead the emphasis of this chapter is on teaching the basic strokes.

Most children who receive swimming instruction while they are in Key Stage 1 will probably not manage to cover all four fundamental strokes, let alone the other five aspects of work listed in the programme of study. Therefore, they are only likely to be able to move on to look at these when they have reached Key Stage 2 and are confident and competent swimmers.

Front crawl

To do the front crawl properly, the swimmer should lie face down on the water in a horizontal, streamlined position so that the water surface is touching her face somewhere between her eyes and her hairline. The swimmer's legs should kick up and down, alternately, in a vertical direction. The swimmer's arms, however, provide the main propulsive force. The arms move alternately and the whole action is continuous. The swimmer's right arm is lifted clear of the water with the elbow leading and her hand should enter the water in advance of her head and slightly to the right of it. The arm should be kept slightly flexed at the elbow so that it creates a downward slant towards the water. The swimmer's fingers should enter the water first and her hand, wrist and elbow start to straighten as she reaches forward to 'catch' the water and to start the pulling/pushing action which will move her hand and arm in a backward direction to the side, then underneath, and then at the side of her body. Once the pulling action is started the swimmer should keep her hand and wrist firm and her elbow bent to create a more effective lever against the water. When the swimmer's right arm passes her right shoulder and begins to change from pushing to pulling, then she will start to lift her left arm from the water to start its part of the stroke.

The swimmer can choose whether to inhale to her right side or left side. The timing of this inhalation, however, is very important and the swimmer must fit it in at the correct part of the stroke. The swimmer should turn her head and breathe in as one arm is starting to pull and the other one is just about to be lifted out of the water. To exhale the swimmer should turn her head so that her face is in the water.

Teaching the stroke

It is helpful for the children if you can give a good demonstration of the arm stroke and the breathing action from the poolside. It would be even better however, if the children could stand on the poolside and watch a competent swimmer demonstrate the stroke while you highlight the essential points. It must be remembered that the most difficult part of this stroke is fitting the breathing into the stroke cycle. Therefore, encourage the children to hold their breath while practising the whole stroke over short distances before incorporating the breathing cycle.

The children can work in stages to build up the stroke beginning with the leg kick.
• Let the children practise pushing off from the side of the pool and gliding out across the water in a streamlined position and with their faces in the water.
• Tell the children to use floats, held at arm's length and then to kick their legs up and down in a scissor action.
• Let them practise this same leg kick at the poolside with one hand on the rail, and one hand flat against the wall. Tell the children

to start their kicking from their hips.
• The children should now practise kicking from their hips as they use floats and move across the water.
• Bring the children back to the poolside and tell them to practise kicking their legs up and down with the emphasis on the upward action. Ask them to *feel* the upward thrust.
• Talk to the children about keeping their ankles 'floppy' as they complete the scissor kick.
• Let the children practise moving across the water, again with their floats, and make sure they practise the teaching points previously outlined.
• Tell the children to hold the rail and the poolside and to practise the leg kick. Ask them now to stretch their feet and to turn them in towards each other as they kick. Their legs should pass each other in a continuous upwards and downwards motion. (The leg going down will usually flex at the knee, but will stay straight as it forces its way upwards through the water from a depth of about 30cm.)
• Encourage the children to think about the soles of their feet as they kick their legs. On the upward kick the sole of the foot should be facing at an angle away from the swimmer and this, if the upward thrust of the leg and the flexibility of the ankle is maintained, will create a propulsive action which will help the swimmer to move forward in the water.

These practices can be exhausting for children and so you should alternate practices against the rail with ones across the pool.

The main teaching points which you should put across to the children are to start the kick from the hips; make long legs; keep the legs close together as they pass each other; keep the ankles so that they are floppy and flexible; extend the toes and point them inwards; keep the legs moving continuously and, finally, to kick up.

Having mastered the leg movement, the children can move on to see how they should use their arms. In the first instance they should be allowed to practise the arm movements while standing in the water.

• Ask the children to stand with one leg in front of the other so that their shoulders are under the water.

• Demonstrate, from the side of the pool, the arm action and ask the children to copy you. Emphasise and hold your arm in the downward entry position so that the children can copy it and so that you can check their arm positions.

• Complete the demonstration and ask the children to complete their strokes. Explain to the children that they should try to 'catch the water', 'pull it down and back' and 'push the water back'.

• Let the children practise the action with one of their arms, then the other and then alternately and continuously.

• Ask the children to bend forwards and put their faces in the water to practise the whole arm stroke.

• Ask the children to walk across the pool and to practise the continuous alternating arm stroke cycle as they walk.

• Tell the children to take a deep breath, hold it, then push off and glide with their faces under the water, kicking their legs, and trying to use the arm stroke.

At the end of the teaching session the children should be aware that when they lift their arms out of the water they should lead the action with their elbows. Also they should know that their fingers must enter the water first and that they should stretch forward with their arms, pulling and then pushing the palms of their hands through the water.

Having mastered the arm action, the children can practise swimming with the leg and arm action together. As they swim they can also practise breathing properly. To begin with they can hold their breath over short distances, but then you can encourage them to try and turn their heads to take one breath as they swim. As they practise they can build up the number of breaths they take until they can breathe with each arm cycle.

Encourage them to turn their heads rather than lifting them and warn them to breathe in carefully at first and blow out forcibly into the water. They should, however, try to keep the whole action smooth and unhurried.

Back crawl

To do the back crawl the swimmer should lie on his back in a streamlined position with the back of his head partially immersed in the water. His tummy should be up on the water while his hips are kept high, but slightly below the water.

The leg action is an up and down kick. This is done on a vertical plane until the arms are used when, because of the slight rotation of the body as the arms pull through the water, the kick is done partly sideways and partly on a vertical plane.

Before the swimmer can kick his leg up, he must bend it at the knee because of the pressure of the water on the lower leg. The leg will drop slightly and then in order to kick up with enough force to cause propulsion, the powerful muscles in the hip have to be worked hard. All the leg muscles are used to move the leg upwards and straighten it, finishing with a whip-like action of the ankle and foot as the toes break the surface of the water. The leg should remain straight for most of the downward movement and the sole of the foot should press down on the water.

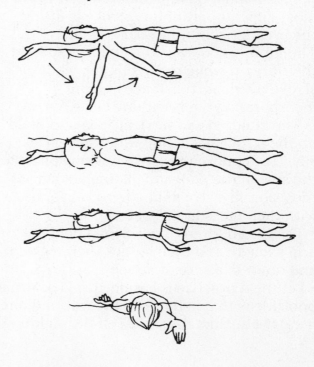

There are two arm actions which can be used to teach back crawl, the bent arm action or 'S' pull and the straight arm action. Usually, the straight arm action is taught to beginners. When using this action the swimmer's hand traces an almost semi-circular pathway through the water. The arm should be kept straight and vertical as it is placed backwards into the water behind the head. The little finger should enter the water first and the palm of the hand should face away from the body as it catches and begins to pull the water. As the hand and arm go deeper into the water the swimmer pulls outward until his hand is parallel with his shoulder. He then pushes his hand, keeping a straight arm, towards his hip to create a strong propulsive force before lifting the arm out and beginning the stroke again.

When the swimmer's right hand is by his right hip the left arm should be starting to pull through the water from above the head.

The swimmer's mouth is clear of the water throughout the whole stroke, even though the back of the head is immersed. Thus most beginners do not worry too much about a particular breathing style.

Teaching the stroke

First teach the children how to regain a standing position after lying on their backs in the water. The children can work with partners who can stand behind them and make shelves with their hands to hold them.

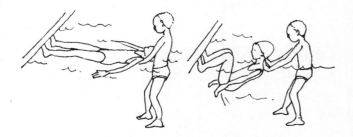

The swimmer should then tuck her feet under the rail at the side of the pool and tuck into a crouched position while holding the rail with both hands. From this position she should gently let go of the rail with her hands, extend her legs and gently lie back in the water until her shoulders rest on her partner's hands.

When she is ready she should regain her crouched position by bending her knees, and reaching forward as she makes a downward and backward movement with her hands, followed by an upward action as she places her feet on the floor to stand up. Her partner can help her by pushing her shoulders forwards when she first starts to move.

The children can then try this manoeuvre using a float. Initially, the float can be used as a pillow which the swimmer can lie on to help build up his confidence.

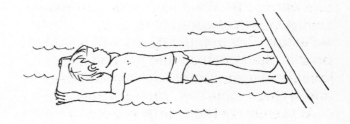

It may also give the swimmer added confidence if his partner is standing by, ready to assist him, when he practises getting back on to his feet.

The children can also use floats to help them practise their leg kicks. They must each hold a float to support their heads and you can encourage them to kick upwards from their hips, making sure they keep their ankles floppy and extend their toes. They can also practise this holding the float on their stomachs. Encourage the children to keep their hips up, their heads back in the water and their eyes on the ceiling.

When the children are more confident they can kick their legs while they use a sculling action with their hands. Emphasise the whip-like action of the ankle as the front of the foot kicks away the water.

The main points which the children should remember are:
- to keep their heads back;
- to keep their eyes looking at the ceiling;
- to keep their tummies up;
- to kick up;
- to move their legs in a continuous action.

Once the children have mastered the leg action they can move on to practise the arm action. It is helpful if they can see a good demonstration of the arm stroke, as you describe the main features to them, before they actually begin to practise it themselves.

It is not possible for the swimmer to practise the arm stroke correctly while standing on the bottom of the pool. However, if they hook one foot under the rail and put the other foot flat against the wall of the pool, the children will be able to lie out in the water to practise the arm stroke. In this way they will be able to concentrate on their arm action without having to worry about their legs. While the swimmers are practising you will be able to provide specific teaching points to individuals as required. Remember to stress to the children the importance of a continuous, rhythmic arm action, moving the arms once to every three leg kicks.

Breaststroke

To do the breaststroke properly the body should be kept as horizontal as possible with the legs trailing under the water. The leg action should be completed without any muscle tension so that the water is not disturbed. The feet are gently drawn up, from the inclined position, towards the swimmer's bottom. As this happens, the swimmer moves her knees forward and outward as they bend, keeping her heels together. To cause propulsion the soles of the feet are turned out and backwards as the heels drive outwards and backwards. The heels then move inwards as the legs return to the streamlined position.

From the streamlined position the swimmer's hands initiate the propulsion. The palms of the hands turn outwards and

the arms pull downwards, outwards and backwards until the arms are slightly in front of, and slightly to the side of, the shoulder line.

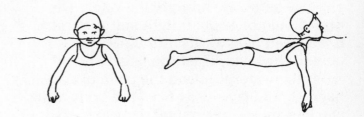

The hands will now be about 30cm below the water surface and the arms will be straight. From now on the remaining movements should be smooth and gentle as the necessary recovery phase of the stroke is completed. The swimmer's arms should now bend at the elbows, the hands should move together so that the thumbs are touching, and the palms of the hands are facing the bottom of the pool. The elbows should be tucked into the sides of the body as the arms are stretched gently into the streamlined position.

Throughout the stroke the swimmer's head should be held still except when the water will rest between the ridge of her nose and her hairline. Inhalation takes place when the swimmer pulls her arms downwards and outwards at the beginning of the arm stroke; and exhalation occurs when the swimmer lowers her head to glide through the water.

When all these actions are carried out for the complete stroke, the sequence of actions for this stroke should be:
- pull and breathe in;
- kick;
- glide and exhale.

Teaching the stroke

Try and provide the children with a demonstration of the whole stroke in the water before they attempt it themselves. If this is impossible, you can show them the arm stroke patterning while everyone is standing on the poolside.

192

Let the children try the whole stroke. They can practise pushing off from the side of the pool and gliding across the water to get into a good streamlined position.

You can then teach the arm action. Let the children practise the arm action while they are standing in the water with their shoulders submerged. Demonstrate the action and highlight the main teaching points. They can then practise walking across the pool while doing the arm action.

Once they have mastered the arm action the children can practise the leg action. Stand on one leg and show the children the action with your other leg. Remember to lean forward so that the demonstration is more realistic. Ensure that the children understand the importance of keeping their feet in the flat-foot position when they drive them backwards and outwards.

They can then practise this action by holding the rail and the poolside. Emphasise the gentle bending of the knees and the forceful kicking action of the soles of the feet and legs. They can then start to push themselves away from the wall, making one or two kicks with their legs and feet. Finally, let the children use a float to hold on to with their arms and hands while they attempt several leg kicks.

The children will need to be able to practise co-ordinating their leg and arm actions in order to achieve the complete stroke. Let them push off from the side of the pool, glide forward and then do one arm pull and one leg kick. Encourage the children to keep their arms extended and close together before they start their arm pulls and to keep their elbows close to their sides during the recovery phase. You should constantly remind the children of the sequence and rhythm of the stroke by saying 'pull and breathe, kick and glide'.

The butterfly stroke

To complete this stroke successfully requires a high degree of swimming ability. To be able to do it, the children will first need to be skilful in performing the other three basic strokes and will, in addition, need strength and body mobility.

To do this stroke properly the swimmer should lie face down in the water in a horizontal position. Both legs move in an upward and downward undulating movement. The upward kick is initiated by the hip muscles and the legs are kept straight as they move upwards. The soles of the feet should press against the water and the legs and feet together create a backward force. After this upward movement, the hips drop in the water and the upper part of the legs move downward. Both knees bend so that the lower legs and feet move upwards towards the surface of the water, then both legs and feet kick downwards until both legs are straight.

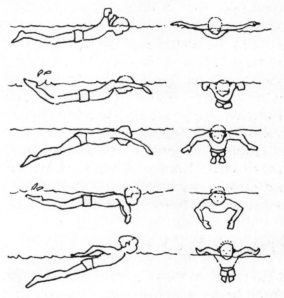

The arms create the main propulsion in this stroke. They are relaxed as they are lifted out of the water and both arms sweep across the water and past the shoulders to start the action. The elbows should be kept higher than the hands and both hands should enter the water at a point in front of the head and on a line just outside the shoulders. The thumbs enter the water first, followed by the palms of the hands which 'catch' the water just underneath its surface with a backward and outward movement which helps to raise the head and chest out of the water. The hands and arms then pull and push the water on either side of the body at a depth of about

193

30–45cm. The arms bend so that both the lower arms and hands move towards each other while they still push the water towards the feet. At the end of this push phase the arms are straightened as they sweep outwards past the hips to start to lift out of the water and to start the next stroke cycle.

When the arms are in the push phase of the arm stroke, the head and shoulders rise out of the water and leave enough clearance between the mouth and the water for the swimmer to both inhale and exhale very quickly and explosively.

This stroke is usually performed with two leg kicks for each arm stroke. The first kick happens just as the hands first enter the water at the beginning of the arm stroke. This kick is very strong, but the second is a weaker kick, occurring during the powerful push phase of the arms.

Teaching the stroke

The children who are introduced to this stroke must be competent, confident swimmers who have no fear of putting their faces in the water and who also have good water stamina. They will need excellent motor co-ordination and above average strength and swimming ability.
• Let the children swim using a breast stroke arm action and the butterfly type leg kick. The children should exaggerate their breast stroke arm action so that their chests clear the water as they pull deeply with their arms, and then ask them to put their heads under the water as they glide.
• Let the children practise a 'mermaid-type' leg kick while they lie on their backs. They should keep both their legs pressed together and try an undulating movement to propel themselves across the water.
• Ask the children to stand in the shallow water and practise throwing both their arms up in the air, across the water and then splashing their whole body on to the water.
• Let the children practise a head-first, surface dive in shallow water to help them become aware of the muscle position and movement needed in the butterfly stroke. To do this, the swimmer should take up a prone position and complete a strong breast stroke arm pull, while at the same time bending sharply at the hips and submerging her upper body downwards in the water. She should, in this one action, succeed in getting her head into a vertical position immediately under her hips. The legs are then lifted into the air above the surface of the water. The whole body should now be inverted in a vertical position and the weight of the body will help it to submerge.
• Tell the children to stand in shallow water with their shoulders submerged and practise the butterfly arm action. The force of the initial arm clearance will drive their bodies on to the water so that they can practise the pull-push action with their arms before standing up again.
• Let the children practise swimming the butterfly arm stroke together with two breast stroke leg kicks so that they begin to feel the rhythm of the stroke.
• Ask the children to practise the arm stroke action as they glide towards the poolside rail.
• Let the children push and glide from the wall and try one arm stroke, before standing up.
• Give the children a float to hold while they practise their leg kick across the water.

Having worked on the elements of the stroke separately, the children can begin to work on co-ordinating their arm and leg actions with their breathing. Ask the children to take a deep breath and push off from the side of the pool. They should glide, and complete two leg kicks followed by one arm stroke. They can then repeat this, but this time trying to complete two whole cycles. Finally, ask the children to try out the whole stroke: bringing their arms over the water, kicking with their legs as they begin the 'catch', pulling with their arms and breathing in and out as they push with their arms and kick with their legs.

Stress the importance of the pull-push phase of the arm stroke and the difference between the two leg kicks. Also remind the children about trying to relax their arms as they swing them across the water.

Survival skills

One way of fulfilling this area of study, as set out in the National Curriculum, would be to use the personal survival skills outlined in the official swimming handbooks. These skills can be used to form a comprehensive programme of work for the children. Survival skills are a purposeful way of not only fostering an interest in swimming, but also of alerting the children to the importance of using these skills in possible emergency situations. One of the first activities which children should learn, which is vital in any emergency situation involving water, is how to keep the body upright with the minimum expenditure of energy by treading water and sculling with the hands.

Treading water

When maintaining an upright position by treading water, the action of the limbs should be minimal and no more effort should be required than that needed to prevent the body sinking. The following are a variety of downwards leg actions which can be used for treading water:
• a breast stroke leg kick;
• a cycling action of the legs bending alternately underneath the body;
• a flutter kick, similar to the front crawl leg kick.

The arms should be used to help keep the body stable by pressing downward towards the bottom of the pool. The hands make sculling actions, moving forcefully away from and towards the centre line of the body.

Sculling

This skill is one which is used not only for survival situations, but also to help to propel the body forward or backward in other swimming activities. The arm action is a smooth movement with the arms and hands moving through a flat figure of eight. The hands should be kept slightly cupped and the palms of the hands turned towards the direction in which they are moving. The figure of eight sculling action should be continuous and any force should be applied in the opposite direction to which the body movement is required.

Floating

Children should also be taught the importance of being able to float in the water with little or no movement. This is a survival technique which may be necessary in some situations where there may be hazards beneath the surface which would prevent the survivor treading water. In some circumstances the technique is used merely to conserve energy. There are three different positions which the children can practise to help them to learn how to float.

The prone float

Using this technique the child should lie face down across the water with her legs extended and her arms stretched out at either side of her head. She should assume a relaxed comfortable position and lift her chin clear of the water when she needs to breathe and then immerse it again to blow out expired air.

The supine float

To float this way the child should lie on his back with his legs extended, his arms by his sides and his eyes, nose and mouth out of the water.

The vertical float

Using this floating technique the child should maintain an upright position in the water by keeping her body vertical and allowing the upthrust of the water to hold her in a state of buoyancy. She should keep her hands at the sides of her body and submerge everything except her mouth, nose, eyes and forehead. In order to breathe in air, she should tilt her head back on to the surface of the water.

Entering unknown waters

As well as being taught 'floating', children should be taught various methods of entering unknown water. In a real emergency, for instance, the children may have to enter the water from a height or to enter water which may have unknown obstacles under its surface. Children should be taught to be ready for these kinds of situations by practising the following methods of entry.

The straddle jump

This method of jumping into water helps to prevent the jumper from sinking and can be practised by jumping out across the water so that the movement, on hitting the water, will be outwards rather than downwards. The jumper should spread his legs and his arms as wide as possible so that when he hits the water his body will make the largest surface impact possible. He should use one foot to take off and his legs should point forwards and backwards 'straddling' the water. His trunk should lean forwards and his arms should be held out sideways.

It will help the children to understand what you mean when describing this method, if you talk about 'striding out across the water' and if you tell them to try to avoid getting their hair wet!

The surface dive

There are two methods of diving from the surface of the water: the head-first dive (as described on page 194) and the feet-first dive. The feet-first dive is safer to use when in unknown waters. The most difficult part, however, is to get the body far enough under the water in order to be able to start to swim. To do this, the arms and the palms of the hands must be thrust upwards through and out of the water, and at the same time the legs should make a powerful downward kick. This action will take the body upwards into a streamlined position and will enable the body to immerse under the water. The body should be quickly tucked and brought into a horizontal position so that the swimmer can begin swimming under the water.

Both these dives should be practised, at this stage, as skills in their own right and, perhaps more importantly, as precursors to both life-saving activities and underwater swimming activities such as scuba diving.

Getting out of the water

Another survival technique which children should practise is getting out of the water. This may seem rather an odd activity to suggest, but if a swimmer has been in cold water for a long time, the final stage of survival could be the most difficult. The children need to realise that in most situations there will not be a set of steps or a convenient hand-rail to help them out of the water. They should, therefore, practise getting out of the water by facing the poolside, putting both their hands flat on to the poolside so that they are shoulder-width apart, and pushing down firmly on to straight arms in order to lift themselves out of the water. They could also practise, if facilities are available, getting on to a large float or pulling themselves out of the water with the assistance of a rope.

Using clothing for floats

The technique used in this method of survival is to trap air inside articles of clothing. Undressing in water can, of course, become a survival skill in itself, since the swimmer has to be able to tread water without the supporting sculling action of the hands which, as was explained earlier, is so important in keeping the body upright and in one position. Trousers are easier to take off than shirts so it is a good idea to do this first. Once the waist is loosened, a flutter kick of the legs will assist the garment to drop downwards to the ankles, to make it easier to take the garments off. When taking off a shirt it is a good idea to undo all the buttons and fasteners first, gather the shirt up to the shoulders, take in a deep breath and quickly slip it over the head. When the garments have been removed they should be spread across the water. All the openings bar one should then be sealed and one of the following methods used to inflate the clothes.

• Hold the opening with both hands and fling the garment into the air so that it fills like a balloon. Bring it down quickly on to the water, holding the aperture with one hand.
• Blow into the garment from the surface of the water until it blows up like a balloon. Then hold on tightly to the opening to trap the air.

When air has been trapped, by either method, the garments can be used as floats to help the survivor to conserve energy. They can be trapped between the knees or ankles, slotted behind the neck like a life-jacket or put under one arm so that the other arm is left free to propel the body.

Hypothermia

All these personal survival techniques are usually practised in a pool where the water and the air temperature is warm, but all children should know how to survive in outdoor situations where the water will almost certainly be much colder than in a swimming pool. They should be given information about hypothermia and be taught to recognise its progressive symptoms:
• shivering excessively;
• muscle rigidity;
• unconsciousness.

A simple diagnosis is that any child, in any situation, whether indoors or outdoors, who looks cold and is shivering excessively should be dried briskly, dressed quickly and be covered in a warm blanket.

Assessing swi~~~
and water skill~

In the programme of study the ~ asked to assess their skills aga~ of criteria such as speed and distance. Children in Key Stage 2 usually enjoy practising their swimming strokes and are often motivated by working for badges or certificates of attainment. In addition, some children like to compete and are interested not only in how well or how far they can swim, but also how fast they can swim. Whenever children show this kind of interest they should be encouraged to swim at speed.

Exploring movement through games

Many children gain water confidence, even when they are non-swimmers, by playing games in the water with their friends. Some of the action songs and ring games which children sing and play in school during Key Stage 1 can be used quite successfully to help children gain confidence in the water and make them aware of some of its properties. For example, they can play 'Ring a ring o' roses', 'Simon says', 'Heads and shoulders, knees and toes', 'Trains' (where the children line up one behind the other, hold each other's shoulders and then move around the pool), the 'Bean game' (see page 38) and 'Numbers' (where you call out a number and the children form groups accordingly, hold hands and walk round in a circle until you tell them to 'scatter' and walk through the water alone).

From simple beginnings like these more competitive games can be introduced.

Frost and sun

This is the same game as the one played on land (see Chapter 7, pages 117–118) but when a child is touched, and has to stand still with her legs wide apart, she can only

...eased back into the game if a
...mmer completes a surface dive between
...he tagged person's legs.

Body parts game

The game proceeds as outlined on page 87, but the children have to go under the water to put the body part on the pool floor.

Back-to-back

The children swim or walk around the pool until the teacher blows his whistle when each child must find a partner and stand back to back in the water. When they are more able swimmers, this game can be played in deeper water where they may then need to tread water to stay upright and link arms in the back to back position.

Shallow water pass-ball

The swimmers are divided up into teams of five. The aim of the game is for each team to make as many successive passes to each other, with a football, before another team intercepts and gains possession of the ball. The team with the most passes at the end of the time allowed is the winner.

Deep water pass-ball

This game proceeds in the same way as described above, but the children will need to swim or tread water all the time.

Arch ball relay

The swimmers are divided up into teams of four and stand one behind the other in their teams. When the whistle blows the first child in the line should pass a ball (size 4), such as a small football, over his head to the second child and so on. When the fourth child receives the ball she should swim on her back with the ball held on her chest to the front of the line. The relay continues until the first child is back in position at the front of the team again. The first team to finish are the winners!

Using swimming and water safety skills to support water-based activities

If children are to become truly aware of the implications of the statement in the National Curriculum referring to the application of swimming skills, then they should be introduced to this awareness in situations which are as near to 'real life' as possible. It is true that they could be given some information, and a question and answer session, or even some role-play situations on these matters and also be given some practice in coping with life-jackets in a swimming pool, but the real awareness will only be assimilated by the children when they are on and in water outdoors. Nobody, for instance, can re-create the initial shock of being upturned from a canoe, a windsurf or a training dinghy into cold water, nor the awful realisation that to survive it might be necessary to either swim the short distance to shore or lie and float on one's back and cope with a life-jacket while steadily getting colder and colder.

Wherever possible, therefore, you should consider taking the older children and exposing them to some outdoor water activities. Ideally, older primary school children could make a short visit to an outdoor activities centre as part of a combined outdoor education programme. But if this is not possible then permission should be obtained and visits made to the nearest 'safe' water where this kind of practice can take place (see Chapter 10 for information on safety during outdoor pursuits).

Chapter 12
Cross-curricular matters

Most primary teachers would both acknowledge and support the notion that they have some responsibility for teaching children certain skills which permeate the whole curriculum. The National Curriculum Council document *Curriculum Guidance 3: The Whole Curriculum* (1990) identifies these cross-curricular skills as those which have as their basis communication, numeracy, study, problem solving, personal and social development, and information technology. This chapter seeks to show how physical education can be used to help develop cross-curricular work; looking at the opportunities available for promoting better integrated learning experiences using physical education.

Communication

Physical education can make significant contributions to the development of the cross-curricular skill of communication. This contribution is particularly evident in Key Stage 1 and for children for whom English is a second language. While the primary object in physical education lessons is not to develop language skills *per se*, it is important to accept that if teachers are responsible for educating the whole child, then they must be aware of the learning potential for language within the physical education environment.

Language is acquired with usage, and lessons in physical education offer children a stimulating environment with wide opportunities for language use. In addition, children are exposed to verbal interactions which are often not necessarily explored elsewhere. There is a special language of operations which can be very complex for a child in the early years at school, for example, 'Please carry the *mat* into the *store area*. We shall need *four* children, one child to carry each *corner* of the mat.'

During physical education lessons the teacher constantly talks about spatial and directional concepts while the children are physically involved in carrying out the actions. Therefore, children are able to experience physically the verbs that are being talked about. Through this increase in understanding of vocabulary and stimulus by involvement in physical education, the children may also develop an ability to vocalise their own feelings. For instance, a reticent child who makes no contribution to classroom discussion or who is unable to write down his thoughts, may find the task of expressing his enjoyable experiences in physical education lessons in written work so much easier.

Certain aspects of language are not taught, but acquired through usage. Many other skills, on the other hand, are learned by doing. In physical education, it is possible to blend both modes of learning in such a way as to help children, not only to understand what they are doing, but to recognise, assimilate and understand the language which helps to make the physical activity possible. If, for example, you were concerned in a particular lesson with the development of motor actions, the language of such actions (for example twist, turn, bend, stretch, swing and jump) must clearly be understood, if the actions are to be achieved. In fitting the language to the action and vice versa, the child practises the physical skill she is developing while at the same time understanding the linguistic feature which describes it. Similarly, the expressive language often used in dance situations can contribute positively in helping children to enrich their language skills. If we ask individual children in a dance lesson to 'creep very smoothly along the ground', or 'whirl and swirl around and around like a tornado' we are not teaching any linguistic figure of speech in a direct way. The very nature of the action, however, gives meaning to the language used and becomes powerfully intertwined with it – the 'doing' reinforces the meaning of the 'saying'. In this way language and meaning develop. When this is embodied in an enjoyable form, such as the context of a well-developed and stimulating lesson, then the learning of language is undoubtedly facilitated. As Joan Tough suggests in her book *Talking and Listening*, 'Fostering communication skills is easier for instance when teachers can promote the use of language in contexts that have immediate or potential interest for the children.'

For older children PE lessons will provide them with many opportunities to illustrate language through movement or to use language as a stimulus for dance (see Chapter 9). There are also many language 'codes', systems of symbols for identification or to communicate information and forms of non-verbal communication, associated with specific activities in physical education, where older children can learn specific sporting language, such as for refereeing or umpiring. For example, when the referee in hockey spreads his arms and calls, '16 yards' or in cricket, 'wide'.

Numeracy

There are many opportunities to reinforce mathematical information during PE lessons in Key Stage 1. The following concepts are only a few examples of how this information can be reinforced.
- 'Line up *one behind the other*.'
- 'Go *over and under* your apparatus.'
- 'Stand at the *side* of your partner.'
- 'Go and collect *one* ball *each*.'
- 'Has *everyone* got *a* bat *each*?'
- 'Make *teams* with *four people* in *each*

team.'
- 'All the people with *blue bands* on, go and sit near the piano.'

Similarly in Key Stage 2, there are many opportunities for numeracy skills to be acquired and reinforced during PE lessons, for example:
- measuring distances and times;
- keeping records of achievements in athletics;
- scoring in games lessons;
- working out strategies and using logic in game-making activities.

Study

At first glance it would seem that PE does not automatically contribute to children's study skills, especially if study conjures up a vision of a child sitting at a desk with his head in a book or with a pencil in his hand. However, contemporary study skills incorporate additional activities such as observation, data collection, recording, making comparisons and judgements, and analysing information. The physical education curriculum stresses the importance of evaluating PE activities from the outset and a key factor in the attainment target for physical education is that children should learn both the skill of observation and the skill of evaluation in reaching the end of each key stage of performance.

It is also generally agreed that **'exercise as a preparation for and recovery from periods of sedentary study, along with the encouragement of good posture, could well help to sustain concentration and commitment and avoid or relieve fatigue and stress'** (*PE for ages 5 to 16*, 1991).

Problem solving

Physical education provides children with the opportunity to acquire and apply problem solving skills in a variety of contexts.
- Games activities: shooting between goal posts. Here, the child is faced initially with the task of deciding where to place the ball in order to kick it, with the correct part of the foot and with enough force and on the correct trajectory to ensure that the ball travels between the posts.
- Swimming: front crawl. In order to create a propulsive force, the child must work out how much force must be exerted by her arm and hand.
- Dance: using a percussion instrument to stimulate rhythmic actions. When working with a partner, the child must consider at what speed the instrument should be played so that his partner can dance effectively.
- Athletic activities: running quickly for 35m. Immediately before the start of this activity, the child must consider how to run straight and how to maintain speed.
- Gymnastic activities: setting up an apparatus arrangement in order to solve a movement task. After considering the nature of the given movement task, the group must work out which pieces of apparatus should be chosen and where they should be placed in relation to each other in order to accommodate each member of the group's movement sequence.
- Outdoor and adventurous activities: mapping in woodlands. Here, the child must solve the problem of representing the information in graphic form and to the correct scale.

The objective is to use teaching methods which are less didactic in style and which actively prompt children to solve problems. If this is done effectively, it should lead to an increasing awareness by the children of the importance of both thinking about and understanding important considerations such as safety.

Personal and social development

Physical education specialists have always claimed a particular role for PE in the personal and social development of children. In PE lessons, particularly lessons where children must work co-operatively with their peers or are faced with competitive situations, they must make a number of decisions and judgements which not only affect themselves, but also other children.

This should lead towards the development of an ability to co-operate with others and to appreciate that satisfaction can be gained from this. Although PE lessons will give children the chance to have fun and enjoy personal success, this is not intended to be at the expense of others.

It is possible, too, for individuals to be given opportunities for general personal development as is clearly articulated in *PE for ages 5 to 16* (1991):
'Teachers can encourage pupils to demonstrate qualities like self-reliance, self-discipline, a spirit of enterprise, a sense of social responsibility, the ability to work alone and with others, a value for and sensitivity towards individual differences, and an ability to apply knowledge in solving practical and real life problems. Co-operative and competitive activities introduce issues concerned with good sporting behaviour, and offer opportunities to learn to distinguish between the good, bad and anti-social including cheating. Pupils can be helped to approach ethical issues which they will meet in their everyday lives and which will help them develop a personal value system.'

Some examples of situations which might arise in physical education contexts are:
• learning to take turns when using gymnastic and games apparatus;
• sharing what might have been a favourite bat or ball with another child, even giving such equipment to the other child and taking a different bat or ball;
• being able to work with a disabled child or one who is perceived to have less ability, particularly in dance and games activities;
• understanding the importance of counting, timing and recording the correct score in athletic and games activities;
• not keeping possession of the ball in soccer or rugby activities;
• being able to keep to rules which have been agreed in various games situations, such as not pushing another child out of the way to gain possession of the ball;
• learning to praise a friend who has succeeded and who might have, for example, achieved a faster sprint time than the child concerned or have scored a goal.

Information technology

Physical education can be linked to information technology but only in a limited way. Children in Key Stage 2 may already be involved in using the software package produced by IBM computers which is linked to the 'Ten Step Award' athletics programme, mentioned in Chapter 8. If so, it will have helped the children to learn how to record and analyse their own athletic performances and in so doing to use and apply their developing information technology skills. For children with special educational needs however, information technology and the development of its relevant skills is especially important in relation to manipulative and visual skills:
'Some game simulations have been specially adapted to encourage children with special needs to develop manipulative and visual skills which they find difficult in other situations' (*PE for ages 5 to 16*, 1991).

Promoting better integrated learning experiences through physical education

'There are several long established, clearly understood and accepted areas of interface between physical education and other school subjects...' (*PE for ages 5 to 16*, 1991).

These areas of interface are listed in *Physical Education for ages 5 to 16* (1991) as:
• health related exercise;
• health education;
• aesthetic education;
• outdoor education;
• safety education.

This section will examine how each of these areas of interface afford opportunities for input from physical education.

Health related exercise

The Health Education Authority's definition of health related exercise, given in *Physical Education for ages 5 to 16* (1991), is 'exercise of the appropriate type, intensity and duration to improve and/or maintain health'.

There has been a growing concern in the UK over recent years that most people in our society do not exercise voluntarily and do not understand the importance to their health of developing a physically active lifestyle. Exercise is fundamental to the all round development of children for the following reasons (taken from *PE in Nursery and Infant School,* 1989):
• Exercise, particularly outdoors, is an essential requirement for healthy growth and development.
• Motor skill learning is essential for survival.
• Motor activity is essential for the strengthening of muscles and bones and for increasing manual dexterity.
• There is a relationship between motor experience and cognitive development.
• Cross limb-eye co-ordination and fine motor-visual co-ordination rely on physical practice.
• Physical activity helps to develop conceptualisation.
• Self concept can be built and established, with the help of the teacher, through successful physical play.
• The social, emotional and moral development of children can be advanced through physical activity with the help and intervention of the teacher.
• Health related exercise and exercise patterns should be developed early in life to prevent heart disease and obesity in later life.
• Exercise develops and maintains optimal functioning of the cardio-vascular system.
• Exercise helps to improve the management of existing disorders such as diabetes and asthma.
• Participation in regular exercise of suitable intensity can decrease the risk of some diseases such as osteoporosis and heart diseases and can lead to increased independence for special groups of people where inactivity could lead to disability or increase a disability.

To accept any or all of these reasons for exercise implies that teachers of primary school children have a responsibility, shared with the children's parents, of making children aware of the importance of an active lifestyle. All children need to understand the contribution that different physical activities can make to their health and to understand that participation and the intensity of participation are long term commitments to a healthy lifestyle. In every PE lesson, it is important that you talk to the children about the health related aspects of what they are doing so that the concepts are reinforced on a regular basis.

Try and make children as active as possible in each lesson, giving them information about those areas of the programme of study where different aspects of health related exercise can be promoted, for example:
'... gymnastics and dance each provide a suitable medium in which to reinforce the knowledge base and experiences associated with flexibility and muscular strength and endurance; games experiences can contribute towards an understanding of cardio-vascular health; both swimming and athletics can contribute to an understanding of cardio-vascular health, flexibility and muscular strength and endurance; and outdoor and adventurous activities provide a test of the

application of this knowledge in various and rapidly changing conditions and contexts' (*PE for ages 5 to 16*, 1991).

Health education

Health education is a whole-school concern and teachers will no doubt be fully conversant with the National Curriculum Council document *Curriculum Guidance 5: Health Education* (1990), which has been endorsed by the Health Education Authority. The Health Education Authority has also published resources on both health related exercise and health education, for example, *Happy Heart 1 & 2* (HEA/Nelson, 1990), *Health for Life 1 & 2* (HEA/Nelson, 1989) and the project pack *My Body* (HEA/Heinemann, 1991).

Happy Heart 1 & 2 are designed to make children more aware of the relationship between physical activity and health and to encourage them to be more active generally, while the *Health for Life* books are concerned with a lifestyles approach to health education. Finally, the *My Body* project consists of a series of units each of which concentrates on a particular bodily function.

The important message for schools is that children have to know how their own health can benefit from a broad, balanced and active physical education programme.

Aesthetic education

Dance provides fruitful opportunities through which children can develop their aesthetic education in the primary school. However, as a subject dance must also share interfaces with music, drama and literature if children are to be inspired into high quality movement. Music and poetry, for instance, can create mood for children's dance, which may awaken and enhance feelings which then transfer into action and ultimately produce aesthetic performances. This integration of the arts is something which children ought to be exposed to as much as possible. The National Curriculum provides another chance to develop

aesthetic education and it is incumbent on teachers not to miss the opportunity!

Outdoor education

The PE Working Group recommended to the National Curriculum Council that outdoor education should be recognised as a whole school concern and become a cross-curricular theme in primary schools. For most children modern living often prevents them from experiencing the most basic of outdoor activities. For example, many children live in traffic congested inner city areas, others live in high-rise flats or in unsafe suburban areas, while others suffer from the restrictions of living on a middle class housing estate with their tidy gardens, neat fences and restricted pathways! If this is the case then only a small percentage of our young children can be said to have access to the freedom to play and be active outdoors.

The previous chapters on outdoor and adventurous activities (see Chapters 5 and 10) have given details about how schools and teachers can provide outdoor experiences for their children within school, the immediate vicinity and different environments. One example of how outdoor physical activities can be integrated into subject areas such as geography and history, in order to bring together knowledge, skills and understanding from several disciplines into a combined and valuable form of direct experience in the field, was given in Chapter 10 where specific reference was made to the link between orienteering activities and the journeys of famous explorers and navigators. Another specific example would be to develop the visit to the seashore suggested in Chapter 10 with:
• a scientific study of beach and sea pollution;
• a geographical exploration of the area including rock formations;
• a biological study of the flora and fauna of the seashore environment.

In addition, combined experiences in the field can help children to develop sensory,

aesthetic and creative appreciation of other environments and, if the activities are well structured, can also provide challenges which will involve problem solving, team work and some independent learning.

'Outdoor education is a medium for bringing together a number of foundation subjects and for forging links across the curriculum. It can develop sound personal and social qualities which are carried into later life. It is worth emphasising that outdoor education is part of our cultural heritage, with its roots in the 'Nature School' of education, the workers educational movements of the nineteenth century and by the 'spirit of quest' or exploration that is so characteristic of our history and achievement' (*PE for ages 5 to 16*, 1991).

Safety education

Teachers have a 'duty of care' in respect of children and are therefore ultimately responsible for their safety; but, teachers should continually aim to make children aware of safety principles for themselves, so that they can make every effort to be responsible for their own safety. It is obvious that many activities in physical education are potentially hazardous unless due care and attention is paid to their planning, organisation and performance. It could be argued that such challenges of the children's courage, initiative and skill and tests of their judgement of what it is safe for them to do are the very essence of physical education.

The general requirements for safe practice in PE have been outlined in the various chapters, particularly the requirements for safety in gymnastics, swimming and outdoor activities. In addition, however, teachers should always pay due care and attention to the possibility of inappropriate use or overuse of the children's bodies. There is always potential risk to the correct development of bones and joints if dangerous movements are attempted or if teachers use ill-founded performance regimes.

Good habits should be adopted very early because they will be relevant to the children for the whole of their lives. Children should therefore be taught how to sit and walk properly and how to pull, push, lift and carry objects correctly.

Safety in physical education can be reinforced during any class lesson on safety, enabling the teacher to explain other aspects of safe practice, such as road safety or safe cycling. Children can also learn how to cope in an accident situation. All children ought to know the procedures for obtaining help within school and then gradually, as the children get older, they should first practise obtaining help from the emergency services and then be shown the basics of emergency aid, which would include resuscitation and treatment of shock, haemorrhaging and choking.

Physical and manipulative skills

Physical education specialists, early childhood educators and those concerned about the development of disabled children are probably surprised that physical and manipulative skills are not included in the list of cross-curricular skills suggested by the National Curriculum Council's cross-curricular document, *The Whole Curriculum* (1990). Earlier discussions in this book have suggested that such skills are vital to the whole development of children, particularly in the early years, and it seems odd that no specific reference has been made to them in the recommendations. The point which needs to be made again therefore, is that 'there is a relationship between motor experience and cognitive development' and that 'gross limb-eye co-ordination and fine motor-visual co-ordination rely on physical practice' (Bruner, 1966 and Furth and Wachs, 1974). In plainer language, children need to use their hands in different ways in as many different contexts as possible if they are to develop the muscles in their fingers, hands, wrists and arms so that they can write, paint, play musical instruments, use the computer, saw, cut, thread, sew, build and do a host of other activities which depend on physical dexterity! To accomplish this, all teachers need to know how these muscles and joints develop and should provide sand and water play, home corner activities, large building blocks, large brush painting activities and so on, so that this can happen. It almost goes without saying that plenty of physical education work is necessary in the earlier years too.

If this practice is seen as valuable for able-bodied children then it is even more important for disabled children. One of the most serious problems for this group, especially those who have started mainstream education, is that they do not have the same rich diet of physical experiences as those which they were often accustomed to enjoy in their special schools. Because of this, they need particular consideration. For them, exercise is crucial, if only to ensure that their physical condition does not deteriorate and compound their disabilities. Opportunities for physical and manipulative skill-work in the classroom, together with suitable physical experiences in physical education lessons, should always be sought for the disabled.

There seems to be little doubt that physical education lessons can provide a suitable context for cross-curricular skills and themes. Imaginative teaching in this respect can make a positive contribution to many aspects of children's learning and should not be ignored. Provided that the importance of physical education as a foundation subject is not diminished much can be done with it to broaden children's developing understanding.

Resources
Bibliography

Introduction

DES *National Curriculum: Draft Order for Physical Education* (1992, HMSO)
DES *Physical Education in the National Curriculum* (1992, HMSO)
DES *Physical Education for ages 5 to 16* (1991, HMSO)
NCC *Non-statutory Guidance (Physical Education)* (1992, NCC)
National Coaching Foundation, *Coaching People with a Disability* (1991, Coachwise)
Powell, K.E. *et al* (1987) 'Physical activity and the incidence of coronary heart disease', *Annual Review of Public Health* Vol.8 pp.253–287
Sleap, M. and Warburton, P. (1990) 'Physical activity patterns in primary school children', *British Journal of Physical Education* (Summer edition)
Sports Council (1988) *Children's Exercise, Health and Fitness*
Sports Council (1992) 'Handicapped Children' – supplement to *Sports Teacher* (Spring)
Welsh Heart Programme Directorate (1987) *Heartbeat Report No.23: Exercise for Health Related Fitness in Wales*
Weltman, A. *et al* (1986) 'The effects of hydraulic resistance strength training in pre-pubertal males', *Medicine and Science in Sports and Exercise* Vol.14 pp.453–456

Gymnastic activities

BAALPE *Safe Practice in Physical Education* (DES approved) (1990, White Line Publishing Services, 60 Bradford Road, Stanningley, Leeds LS28 6EF)
DES *Mathematics in the National Curriculum* (1989, HMSO)
DES *National Curriculum Physical Education Working Group Interim Report* (1991, HMSO)
McNaught-Davis, P. *Flexibility: How to understand it, How to achieve it* (1991, Partridge Press)

Games

Mini Hockey Rules (1990, All England Women's Hockey Association)
Netball Rules for Young Players (1991, All England Netball Association)
Asquith, A. 'Teaching Games for Understanding' in *Issues in Physical Education in the Primary School* (1989, Falmer)
Brackenridge, C. *Lacrosse: an individual skills programme* (1991, Pavick Publications Sheffield Polytechnic)
Brown, A. *Active Games for Children with Movement Problems* (1990, P. Chapman Publications)
Cooper, A. *The Development of Games Skills: scheme work for teachers* (1982, Blackwell)
Cooper, M.J. (1977) *Observational Studies in Nursery School* (Unpublished PhD Thesis) Durham University
Downey, J. (Director of Coaching, Badminton Association of England) *Short Badminton Handbook* (1991, BAE)
English Basketball Association *The Passers Manual* (1986, YMCA)
ESFA Guide to the Teaching of Soccer in Schools (1988, English Schools Football Association)
Rules of Mini Volleyball (1988, English Volleyball Association)
Gillham, B. *Handicapping Conditions in Children* (1989, Routledge)
Hutt, C. *Males and Females* (1972, Penguin)
Kalbfleisch, S.E. *Skip to it* (1985, A&C Black)
Guide to the Introduction of Short Tennis for Teachers (1984, Lawn Tennis Association)
Matterson, E.M. (Ed.) *This Little Puffin: finger plays and nursery songs* (1991, Penguin)
Parratt, A.L. *Indoor Games and Activities* (1982, Hodder & Stoughton)

Primary Focus – quarterly magazine of the Physical Education Association, see particularly 1990/91 issues
New Image Rugby (1988, RFU) – book and video
Taylor, D. *Dancing Rhymes* (1975, Ladybird Books) *Out of print*
Warburton, P. and Wetton, P. *Two Surveys of the Motor Performance of Infant Aged Children* (1991, DES)
Wetton, P. *Bright Ideas: Games for PE* (1987, Scholastic Publications Limited)

Athletic activities

Steele, J. & Wetton, P. 'News update: Boys do better at sports from an early age survey shows' *Child Education* No.11 (1988, Scholastic Publications Limited)

Dance

Let's Move, Time to Move and *Dance Workshop* BBC Radio 5 – details available from BBC Education Information Department
Arnold, J. (Ed.) *Say it Again Granny!* (1986, Bodley Head) *Out of print*
Bruce, V.R. *Movement and Dance in the Primary School: Into the nineties* (1988, OUP)
Eliot, T.S. *Collected Poems of T.S. Eliot 1909–1962* (1976, Faber and Faber)
English Folk Dancing and Song Society *English Folk Dancing in the Primary School* (1960, Novello) – booklet and LP record
Animals on the Move (Level 8 extension readers) (1984, Ginn)
Harrison, K. *et al Bright Ideas: Dance and Movement* (1989, Scholastic Publications Limited)
Harrison, K. *Look! Look what I can do* (1986, BBC)
Hughes, T. *The Iron Man* (1989, Faber and Faber)
Ireson, B. (Ed.) *Young Puffin Book of Verse* (1989, Penguin)
Johnson, J.W. *God's Trombones: seven Negro sermons* (1991, Penguin 20th C. classics)
Learning with … Rhymes (1976, Ladybird Books) *Out of print*
Lewis, C.S. *The Lion, the Witch and the Wardrobe* (1980, Fontana Lions)
McGough, R. *Sky in the Pie: a book of new poems* (1985, Penguin)
Moore, G. (Ed.) *Illustrated Poets: Robert Frost* (1988, Aurum Press)
Maypole and Country Dancing Cassettes 1 & 2 with instructions (The Nottingham Group)
Owen, G. *Salford Road* (1992, Fontana)
Owen, G. *Song of the City* (1985, Armada)
Reeves, J. *The Autumn Book* (1977, Heinemann)
Shakespeare, W. *Macbeth* Hunter, G.K. (Ed.) (1989, New Penguin Series)
Shreeves, R. *Children Dancing: practical approach to dance in the primary school* (1990, Ward Lock Educational)
Woodland, E.J.M. (Ed.) *Skipping Susan* (1979, HarperCollins Educational)
Wylie, E. *Last Poems* (1982, Academy/Chicago)

Outdoor and adventurous activities

DES *Geography in the National Curriculum* (1991, HMSO)
DES *Learning Out of Doors* (1985, HMSO)
DES *Playground Safety Guidelines* (1992, HMSO)
DES *Safety in Outdoor Education* (1989, HMSO)
National Curriculum Council Consultation Report (1991, NCC)

Swimming

Amateur Swimming Association *Swimming Teaching and Coaching (Level 1)* (1991, ASA)

Cross-curricular matters

HEA *Happy Heart 1 & 2* (1990, HEA/Nelson)*
HEA *Health for Life 1 & 2* (1989 HEA/Nelson)*
*Available from Thomas Nelson & Sons Limited
HEA *My Body* (project pack) (1991, HEA/Heinemann), available from Heinemann Educational
NCC *Curriculum Guidance 3: The Whole Curriculum* (1990, NCC)

NCC *Curriculum Guidance 5: Health Education* (1990, NCC)
Tough, J. *Talking and Listening* (1980, Ward Lock)
Wetton, P. *P.E. in Nursery and Infant School* (1989, Routledge and Kegan Paul)

Useful addresses

All England Netball Association Netball House, 9 Paynes Park, Hitching, Herts. SG5 1EH
All England Women's Hockey Association Coaching Office, 10 Parsonage Street, Dursley, Glos. GL11 4EA – 'Hockey Stix Award' proficiency award scheme pack available
All England Women's Lacrosse Association Unit 4, Western Court, Bromley Street, Digbeth, Birmingham B9 4AN
Amateur Athletic Association of England Edgbaston House, 3 Duchess Place, Hagley Road, Edgbaston, Birmingham B16 8NM – 5 Star Awards
Amateur Swimming Association Harold Fern House, Derby Square, Loughborough, Leics. LE11 0AL
Badminton Association of England The National Badminton Centre, Bradwell Road, Loughton Lodge, Milton Keynes, Bucks. MK8 9LA
BBC Education Information BBC White City, 201 Wood lane, London W12 7TS
BARB/AGB: Broadcasters Audience Research Board, Glenthorne House, Hammersmith Grove, London W6 0ND Audience of Great Britain (Taylor Nelson Group Limited), West Gate, Hangar Lane, Ealing, London W5 1UA
British Sports Association for the Disabled Solecast House, 13–27 Brunswick Place, London N1 6DX
Continental Sports Paddock, Huddersfield, W. Yorks. HD1 4SD
English Basketball Association 48 Bradford Road, Stanningley, Leeds LS28 6DF
English Folk Dancing and Song Society Cecil Sharp House, 2 Regents Park Road, London NW1 7AY
English Schools Athletic Association Award Scheme (presently sponsored by TSB) c/o 26 Coniscliffe Road, Stanley, Co. Durham DH9 7RF
English Schools Football Association 4A Eastgate Street, Stafford ST16 2NQ
English Volleyball Association 27 South Street, Westbridgford, Notts. NG2 7AG
Health Education Authority Hamilton House, Mabledon Place, London WC1H 9TX
Heinemann Educational Customer Services Department, Halley Court, Jordan Hill, Oxford OX2 8EJ
Kwik Cricket Office Lords Cricket Ground, London NW8 8QZ Kwik Cricket Action Line: 071 289 2419. Kwik Cricket play equipment available from the Kwik Cricket Office
National Coaching Foundation 4 College Close, Beckett Park, Leeds LS6 3QH
National Rounders Association Mr B. MacKinney, Administration Secretary, c/o 3 Denehurst Avenue, Nottingham NG8 5DA
The Nottingham Group Ludlow Hill Road, Westbridgford, Nottingham NG2 6HD
Physical Education Association Ling House, Unit 5, Western Court, Bromley Street, Digbeth, Birmingham B9 4AN
RFU Rugby Road, Twickenham TW1 1DZ
Royal Life Saving Society UK Mountbatten House, Studley, Warwickshire, B80 7NN
Short Tennis Department Lawn Tennis Association Trust, Queen's Club, Palliser Road, West Kensington W14 9EG Sports Council 16 Upper Woburn Place, London WC1H 0QP
Swimming Teachers Association Anchor House, Birch Street, Walsall, West Mids W52 8HZ
The Swim Shop 52–58 Albert Road, Luton, Beds. LU1 3PR
Ten Step Award Scheme – starter pack including computer programmes, videos, list of local agents available from Mr L. Emmence, National Administrator for Ten Step Award Scheme, 'Prosit', Rosedowns Road, Medstead, Hants. GU34 5LG
Thomas Nelson & Sons Limited Nelson House, Mayfield Road, Bolton-on-Thames, Surrey KT12 5PL

Music

Key Stage 1

Appalachian Spring Copland, A. (1944)
La Carnaval des animaux (The Carnival of the Animals) Saint-Saens, C. (1886)
'Clown's Dance' from *Circus* Ibert, J. (1952) (from the film *Invitation to the Dance*, 1954)
Circus Polka (for a young elephant) Stravinsky, I. (1942)
'Coming round again' on *Greatest Hits Live: Carly Simon* Simon, C. (1988, Arista)
'Dance of the Tumblers' from *Snow Maiden* Rimsky-Korsakov, N.A. (1881)
Danse Macabre (Op.40) Saint-Saens, C. (1874)
'The Grasshopper's Dance' by Bucalossi/ Hylton, J. *Hello Children Everywhere Vol.1* Various Artists (1988, EMI)
Greensleeves (1580) e.g., *Fantasia on Greensleeves* Williams, V. on 'The Classic Experience' (1988, EMI)
Mock Morris Grainger, P. (1910)
'Morning' from *Peer Gynt* Suite No.1 (Op.46) Grieg, E. (1888)
The Nutcracker Tchaikovsky, P.I. (1892)
'Overture' from *Candide* Bernstein, L. (1956)
Pastoral Symphony No 6 in F major (Op.68) Beethoven, L. (1807)
Radetzky-Marsch (Op.228) Strauss, J. (the elder) (1848)
'Spring in E major' from *The Four Seasons* Vivaldi, A. (1725)
The Stars and Stripes Forever Sousa, J.P. (1897)
'Summertime' Gershwin, G. & I. on *George Gershwin Collection*, Various Artists (1987, Deja Vu)
'Swing Low Sweet Chariot' from *Spirituals* sung by H.E. Porter and his gospel singers.
'Take Five' Desmond, P. & Brubeck I. on *Take... The Greatest Hits* Dave Brubeck (1991, Elite/Pickwick)
'You make me feel (mighty real)' (reissue) Sylvester (1989, Southbound)

Key Stages 1 & 2

'Adagio for Strings' from *String Quartet in B minor* Barber, S. (1936)
BBC Sporting Themes, Various Artists (1988, BBC/Pickwick)
'Just be good to me' on *Rapping with the Ladies* Shabba Ranks (1990, Greensleeves)
'Ritual fire dance' from *El amor brujo* De Falla, M. (1915)

Key Stage 2

'Aase's Death' and 'Anitra's Dance' from *Peer Gynt* Suite No.1 (0p.46ii) Grieg, E. (1875)
'Air on a G String' from *2nd movement 3rd Orchestral Suite in D* Bach, J.S. (c1723)
'Arrival of the Queen of Sheba' from *Solomon* Handel, G.F. (1748)
CATS Lloyd Webber, A. (1981, Polydor)
Chariots of Fire Vangelis, O.P. (1981, Polydor)
'Clair de lune' from *Suite bergamasque* (Third movement) Debussy, C. (1890)
'Crises' Oldfield, M. from *Crises* (1983, Virgin)
'Flight of the Bumble Bee' from *The Tale of Tsar Saltan* Rimsky-Korsakov, N.A. (1899-1900)
'Graceland' Simon, P. from *Graceland* (1986, Warner Brothers)
Joseph and the Amazing Technicolor Dreamcoat Lloyd Webber, A. and Rice, T. (1974 MCA)
'Mars' from *The Planets Suite* Holst, G. (1918)
La Mer Debussy, C. (1905)
'O fortuna' from *Carmina Burana* Orff, C. (1937)
Requiem Verdi, G. (1874)
'Rustle of Spring' Sinding, C. (1856) on *The World of Piano* (1992, DECCA)
The Sorcerer's Apprentice Dukas, P. (1987)
'Too many Broken Hearts in this World' Donovan, J. on *Ten Good Reasons* (1989, PWL)